Volume 17

RESISTANCE
SEXTANT

THE NEW
how it works

*Heating materials with radio waves of high frequency
is being used in the experimental production
of metallic glass ribbon.*
Photo: Paul Brierley

THE *NEW* ILLUSTRATED
Science and Invention
ENCYCLOPEDIA

H. S. STUTTMAN INC. PUBLISHERS · WESTPORT, CONNECTICUT 06889

Contents

Volume 17

Published by H. S. STUTTMAN INC.
Westport, Connecticut 06889
© Marshall Cavendish Limited 1987, 1989

Library of Congress Cataloging in Publication Data
Main entry under title:

The New Illustrated Science and Invention Encyclopedia

Includes index.
Summary: An alphabetical encyclopedia covering all aspects of science, the physical world, mechanics and engineering.
1. Science—Dictionaries. 2. Engineering—Dictionaries. [1. Science—Dictionaries 2. Engineering—Dictionaries] I. Clarke, Donald. II. Dartford, Mark. III. Title: How It Works.
Q123.I43 1987   503'.21   85-30973
ISBN 0-87475-450-X

Resistance

Resistance can be defined as an opposition to motion, leading to a dissipation of ENERGY. Many physical systems rely on the application of some physical influence to produce some form of motion, such as the motion of electrons in an electric context or the motion of objects in mechanics.

In such circumstances the applied physical influence does not produce unlimited motion. The desired effect is limited by some internal opposition within the system.

Electric resistance

When an electromotive force (emf, measured in volts) is applied to a metal, electric CONDUCTION takes place – an electric current flows through the material, caused by the movement of negatively charged ELECTRONS.

Although a conductor of electricity allows current to flow, it does not flow with complete freedom. Collisions occur between the moving electrons and the atoms of the material to interfere with the electron flow. This phenomenon is termed *electric resistance*. Materials differ in their ability to inhibit electron flow and this property is measured by the *resistivity* or *specific resistance* of the material.

The total resistance of a conductor, for example a metal wire, depends on the resistivity of the metal, the length of the wire and the cross-sectional area of the wire. Resistance is directly proportional to length and inversely proportional to the area of cross section.

In a circuit carrying an alternating current, the total opposition to current flow is termed the *impedance,* which includes capacitive and inductive REACTANCE, in addition to the resistance.

In 1826, G. S. Ohm established that, in conditions of constant temperature, the current flow in a conductor is proportional to the applied voltage, the constant of proportionality (voltage divided by current) being resistance or, for alternating current, the impedance of the electric circuit.

At low temperatures, conductors show little or no resistance – they exhibit SUPERCONDUCTIVITY.

Magnetic resistance

Magnetism is considered to have lines of magnetic force or *flux* passing through the material in which it is produced. Materials differ in the intensity of magnetization produced within them by a magnetic field. The magnetic intensity is measured as a ratio termed the *susceptibility* of the magnetic material.

Magnetism can be produced in a material by an electric field (ELECTROMAGNETISM) or by the effect of a secondary magnetic field (*magnetic induction*). The degree to which a material responds to a magnetizing influence is termed its *permeability*. A magnetic material is usually characterized by its *relative permeability,* which is the ratio of the flux density produced in the material to the flux density produced in a vacuum (or air, for most practical purposes) by the same magnetic field.

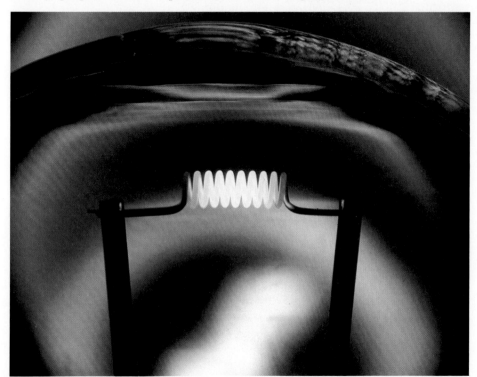

Right: Magnification reveals the structure of a high-resistance tungsten filament. This filament is a simple coil, unlike the coiled coil structure commonly used in household light bulbs. When an electromotive force is applied to the metal coil, the electric conduction which takes place causes the filament to give off energy in the form of light and heat. Energy is dissipated only in the coil, but not at its ends.

Above: A test on an insulating material shows that voltage breakdown occurs when the binding energy of the material is overcome by high temperatures and the electrons are free to move.

By analogy with electromotive force (emf or voltage) in an electric circuit, the effect producing the magnetic flux is the magnetomotive force (mmf), and the ratio between the magnetomotive force and the magnetic flux produced is called the *reluctance* of the magnetic circuit.

Electrostatic resistance

If an INSULATOR is placed between two metal plates, a CAPACITOR is formed. When the metal plates are at different electric potentials, as a consequence of an applied voltage, the system becomes a store of electric charge, and a field of electric force is set up in the insulator between the plates.

The electric field strength within the capacitor is the ratio of the voltage difference between the plates to the distance between the plates and is measured in units such as volts per foot. The electric flux is produced as a force between opposite charges on the two plates and the flux density is the ratio of the charge difference to the area of the metal plates. Electric flux density, or *electric displacement,* is measured in units such as coulombs per square foot.

The permittivity of a material is measured by comparing the flux density with the strength of field producing the flux. Comparison between materials is customarily made in terms of their relative permittivity, which is the CAPACITANCE of a system with the material between the plates divided by the capacitance of the same condenser with air between the plates.

Mechanical resistance (friction)

When two solid surfaces are in contact, there is always some resistance to the motion of one surface relative to the other, however smooth the surfaces.

This resistance to motion, produced largely by the irregularities on one surface interlocking with those on another, is called friction. When a force is applied to a mechanical system in an attempt to produce motion between two surfaces, a force of friction, called static friction, is brought into play which opposes motion up to a limit depending on the contact surfaces. The friction at this limiting stage is termed *limiting* friction. Once motion has been established, the system requires a reduced amount of force to maintain this motion. The force then being overcome is termed *sliding* or *dynamic* friction.

The force needed to overcome friction between any pair of surfaces is proportional to the force pressing the surfaces together, and the ratio between these forces is called the *coefficient of friction* for that pair of surfaces.

Resistance in fluids (viscosity)

When liquids or gases are in motion, internal friction forces cause a resistance to the fluid motion. This resistance to flow is called viscosity. Free flow is the result of low viscosity, and a less-mobile fluid has a higher viscosity. Viscosities of different fluids are compared in terms of a *coefficient of viscosity,* which is directly analogous to electric resistivity.

The internal resistive forces in liquids result from intermolecular cohesion forces opposing any externally applied force. When heated, the liquid molecules gain kinetic energy and the cohesion forces are reduced – the viscosity is reduced when the liquid temperature is raised.

Overcoming resistance

When a physical influence moves or produces movement in any situation, work is done. The performance of work requires that energy be provided. This supplied energy must, however, overcome any resisting influences before the desired movement or effect can be achieved. So the supplied energy must be greater than the energy required to produce the desired end result, the excess energy being dissipated in overcoming the resistance of the system.

See also: Capacitor; Insulator, electric.

Resistor

A resistor is a device used to set the relationship between voltage and current in an electric circuit. The value of a resistor is known as its resistance and is measured in *ohms*. Most resistors are linear – they obey OHM'S LAW, but some designs alter their value sharply when current is passed and are, therefore, used as protection against electric surges.

When current is passed through a resistor, power is dissipated, appearing as heat. To avoid damage to the resistor, its size and construction must be sufficient to withstand a specified amount of POWER (measured in *watts*). For this reason, there is a wide diversity of resistors manufactured, ranging from those suitable for dissipating a fraction of a watt, such as is encountered in a transistor radio, television set or electric clock, up to very large constructions capable of handling kilowatts, for example, in power plants.

Manufacture of resistors

A large number of resistors are used in the various branches of electronics. Most of these are mass produced at low cost and have relatively poor tolerances in their values. For precise applications, more expensive alternatives are available.

The *carbon composition resistor* is mass produced in extremely large numbers for a wide range of applications. The methods and materials used are cheap and simple. The resistive component consists of finely powdered carbon black dispersed in an inert filler, such as fireclay. The powders are mixed together in proportions corresponding to the final

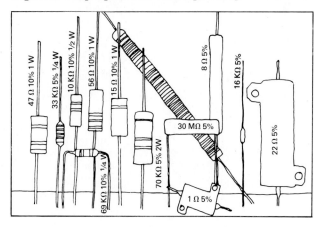

Below: A selection of resistors, showing the range in size, resistance value (above), construction, and color coding. The amount of energy a resistor can handle safely is its rating in watts. For large wattages, metal fins are added to dissipate the heat.

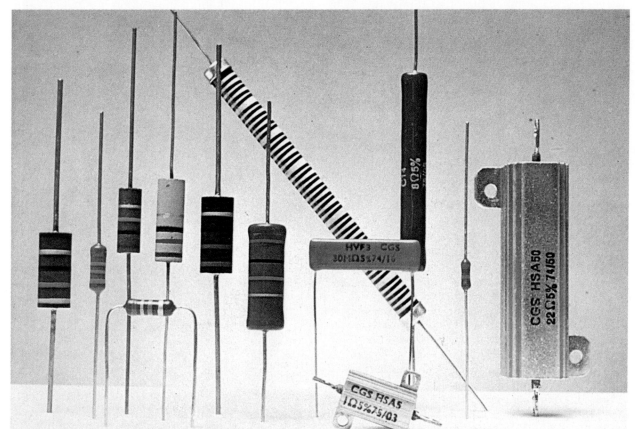

Above: Thick-film resistors mounted on a printed circuit board. The resistance valves have been precisely adjusted by using a laser beam to make fine cuts, which increase the effective length.

resistance values desired, and a liquid resin binder is added. The individual resistors are formed by hot pressing the mixture into rods and molding them into insulating sleeves with tinned copper leads. A final heat treatment hardens the casing and completes the curing of the resistive mixture. The components are then automatically tested and categorized according to the value of tolerance. The final stage of manufacture is to paint the resistor in bands corresponding to a color code. The band nearest to the end represents the first number of the value; the second band the second number and the third band the number of zeros. Gold or silver bands indicate the value tolerance of the component.

High-precision fixed resistors are made by deposition of a film of resistive material onto a base, usually a ceramic. The film may be made from a number of materials. One of the commonest is carbon, but tin oxide is also in widespread use. For very high precision components, an extremely thin layer of metal ALLOY, such as one of nickel and chromium known commercially as Nichrome, is deposited on the base by a vacuum process.

All these types of resistor have in common the fact that they can dissipate considerably more power than a carbon resistor of the same size, because of the thermal properties of the material on which they are based. The values can be adjusted to within close tolerances by a method called *spiraling*. A shallow groove in a form similar to a screw thread is cut in the surface of the resistor body, effectively lengthening the distance between its ends and increasing the value. Very high precision resistors are also made by winding fine resistance wires onto a tubular ceramic body and then covering them with vitreous enamel to give them high stability even at extremely high temperatures.

RESISTOR COLOR CODE

47,000 Ω 5%

1st digit 2nd digit Number of zeros Tolerance

Color		1st digit	2nd digit	No of zeros	Tolerance
Black	●	–	0	–	–
Brown	●	1	1	0	1%
Red	●	2	2	00	2%
Orange	◐	3	3	000	3%
Yellow	○	4	4	0,000	4%
Green	●	5	5	00,000	–
Blue	●	6	6	000,000	–
Purple	●	7	7	0,000,000	–
Gray	◐	8	8	00,000,000	–
White	○	9	9	000,000,000	–
Gold	◐	–	–	–	5%
Silver	○	–	–	–	10%
No color		–	–	–	20%

Above: An international color code is printed on all resistors so that their value and accuracy are readily apparent. The resistor shown above, for example, has a value of 47,000 ohms, and this value can vary by ±5 per cent. The design of a circuit that includes this resistor must allow for its value being between 44,650 Ω and 49,350 Ω.

Variable resistors, usually known as potentiometers (or *pots* for short) can be made in various ways. In all of these, a moving contact slides along the surface of a resistance wire wound on a former or a resistive glaze printed onto a ceramic base.

Resistors based on glazes are known as *thick film* resistors. A paste, consisting of a resistive material, usually an oxide of ruthenium, one of the rarer precious metals, glass powder and a cellulose-based binder to give the correct flow properties is screen printed onto a ceramic plate or substrate. Careful heat treatment at temperatures up to about 1830° F (1000° C) burns off the cellulose, melts the glass and forms a glaze in a pattern which was defined by the screen used to print it. The method is based on two ancient crafts, *screen printing* as a form of art and the *glazing* of pottery to form porcelain. The process is inexpensive and capable of large-scale production for individual resistors and for networks of more than one component – a form of INTEGRATED CIRCUIT.

See also: Alloy; Ceramics; Electricity; Energy; Integrated circuit; Potentiometer; Power; Resistance; Semiconductor; Switch.

Resonance

Resonance is a sudden, large increase in the amplitude of a vibrating system in response to a series of imposed vibrations at a certain frequency. It is a characteristic of all OSCILLATORS. In many physical systems, particles disturbed by some external influence or force vibrate or oscillate about their original position. When left alone after the initial disturbance, the range of movement each side of the rest position (the amplitude) gradually decreases as the particle energy is dissipated in overcoming the resistance to motion. This decrease of amplitude is termed *damping*.

The number of oscillations that a particle performs in one second is termed the frequency of vibration, and any such physical system has a certain characteristic or *natural frequency* of vibration called the *resonant frequency* of the system. This is determined by the physical quantities involved, namely the type of medium and the physical dimensions of the system.

If the system is disturbed in a regular repetitive manner, instead of being allowed to vibrate naturally, it will be forced to vibrate at the frequency of the disturbing force rather than at its own natural frequency. If, however, the forcing frequency coincides with the natural frequency of the system, then the amplitude of the vibration becomes large and the energy supplied by the forcing vibration becomes a maximum. This condition of maximum energy transfer is termed resonance, and it has many important consequences, particularly in mechanics, acoustics and electronics.

Mechanical resonance
A simple example of resonance in a mechanical system is that of pushing a child on a swing. Resonance and maximum amplitude are achieved if a push is applied to the swing at the same frequency as that with which the swing is oscillating – if it is pushed each time it reaches the end of its path. Any attempt to push the swing at any other frequency will be comparatively inefficient because the push may miss the swing occasionally or oppose the momentum of the system. The principle is the same as that of a pendulum.

Another simple example is that of a diver on a springboard. As the diver jumps up and down to gain height for the dive, a stage is reached where the frequency of the periodic downward force practi-

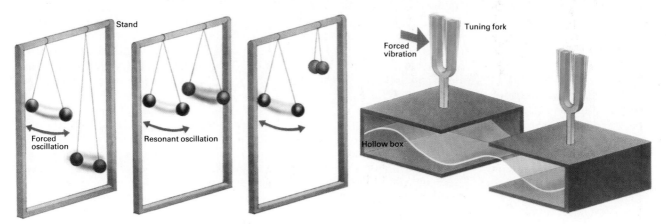

Above: Three views of moving pendulums. If the pendulums are of different lengths, motion in one has little effect on the other. Resonance (maximum swing) occurs when the pendulums are the same length. Below: A column of air resonating in a tube. The tube is closed, so air at the ends is stationary, forming nodes. Midway between the nodes (at antinodes) the air has maximum movement. The ends of an open tube (below) will always be places of maximum air movement. This tube is shown resonating at its second harmonic (with two nodes within the tube). Resonance can occur between identical tuning forks (above) mounted on separate hollow boxes, the open ends facing each other. Sound from one tuning fork travels to the other box, making the other fork vibrate.

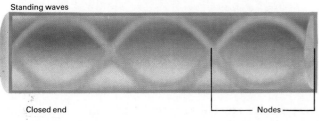

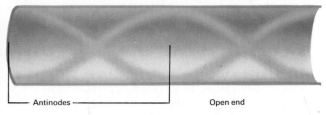

Above: Wind instruments, such as this bass tuba emit a large range of notes when columns of air are made to resonate by the opening of valves.

cally coincides with the natural frequency of the board. The amplitude of vibration then becomes large and the periodic force is said to have set the board in resonance.

The energy absorbed by a system at resonance can be destructively large when periodic forces act on the structure. For example, soldiers marching in step over a bridge can provide a periodic forcing influence at a frequency coincident with the natural frequency of the structure. If this occurs, the bridge absorbs excessive energy produced by resonance, and the resulting large amplitude of vibration can cause collapse.

There are several recorded instances of bridge collapse, and it has long been established practice for soldiers to break step when crossing a bridge. Probably the most famous and most dramatic bridge collapse resulting from resonance was of the suspension bridge across the Tacoma Narrows in Washington State in 1940. In this instance the destructive resonance was induced in the bridge by a wind gusting at the critical frequency.

Acoustic resonance
If a vibrating tuning fork is held near an open air cavity or column of which the natural frequency, determined by its geometry, equals the frequency of the vibrating fork, a much louder sound comes from the mass of air than from the fork itself.

This increase is the result of STANDING WAVES, produced in the cavity. When the cavity length is tuned to the wavelength of the vibration, the sound waves are repeatedly reflected from the cavity ends, giving an amplifying effect – resonance. If the cavity end is closed, reflection occurs at the point in the standing wave of minimum displacement – the *node*. An open end gives reflection at the point of maximum displacement – the *antinode*.

This phenomenon in air columns is of prime importance in the design of wind instruments. The pitch of a note emitted by an air column is controlled by altering the length of the resonating cavity. An organ consists essentially of a large number of pipes of different resonant frequencies which can be separately selected. In brass instruments, the column length is increased by the opening of valves, giving access to further sections of tube, and in woodwind instruments, although the physical length is fixed, the effective length is varied by opening and closing holes or valves.

The suppression or avoidance of unwanted resonances is a major consideration in the design of loudspeaker enclosures and in the acoustic design of rooms and halls for various purposes.

Resonance in electric circuits
The phenomenon of resonance finds important application in electric circuits, such as the tuning of a

radio receiver. Tuning involves the absorption of energy from the transmitted radio waves, but only waves of a frequency corresponding to the desired station are of interest.

The behavior exhibited by certain components in an electric circuit when subjected to an alternating current or voltage is frequency-dependent. Examples are the INDUCTANCE of a coil and the CAPACITANCE of a *capacitor*. When an inductor and capacitor are connected together in parallel, a resonant circuit results. The resonant frequency depends on the values of inductor and capacitor. If the incoming signal is supplied to a coil, having inductance and electric resistance, connected in series with a capacitor, and the capacitance is varied, then a condition can be achieved where the inductance equals the capacitance at a particular frequency.

This frequency becomes the resonant frequency of the circuit and current flow is maximized, which results in the receiver having a loud response to waves at the frequency of interest. So the circuit accepts a particular frequency preferentially and is frequently referred to as an *acceptor* tuning circuit. If

Below: Resonance between atoms is utilized in a nuclear magnetic resonance spectrometer. The resonant frequencies of a sample are plotted to help determine the chemical composition.

the circuit elements are joined in parallel instead of in series, then a similar condition occurs on tuning, except that voltage is maximized and the current minimized. This effect minimizes the response of the receiver to the particular resonant frequency, and the circuit is termed a *rejector*. Acceptor and rejector circuits are often used in conjunction to tune a desired frequency response free from nearby interfering frequencies.

Other resonance applications

Any physical system capable of vibration will resonate under the action of an impulse of the appropriate frequency. Atomic or molecular systems, which consist of vibrating particles, for example electrons, will resonate.

A range of techniques has been developed in which resonance effects between such systems and suitable periodic impulses are used for the identification and structure determination of complex molecules: they can also provide detailed information regarding the atomic characteristics of an examined material.

Nuclear Magnetic Resonance (NMR) and Electron Spin Resonance (ESR) are the best-known techniques in this category.

See also: Inductance; Oscillator; Wave motion.

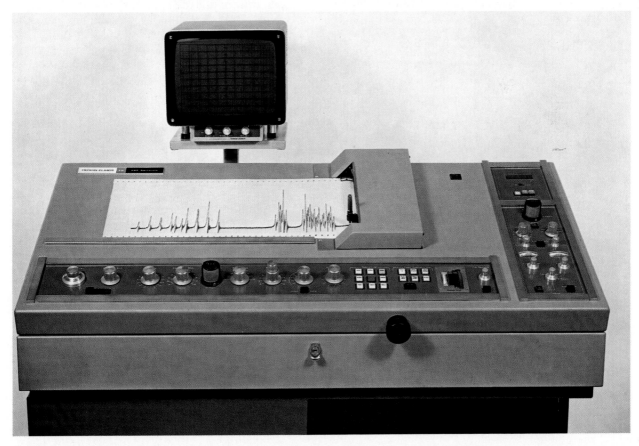

Revolver

A revolver is a firearm in which a series of barrels, or a cylinder with a series of chambers bored centrally through it, revolves about a central axis. In this way each barrel or chamber, containing a cartridge, may be presented to the firing mechanism in turn. In the case of the cylinder containing the chambers, each chamber is aligned with a single barrel as it reaches the firing mechanism. The revolver can be a pistol, a shoulder gun or a machine gun, and the first specimens appeared before the close of the sixteenth century. These early models were nearly all pistols and today the term revolver is taken generally to mean a particular type of repeating pistol.

In the earliest models, the charges proved extremely difficult to ignite. Matchlocks and flintlocks were not designed to work in any position other than upright, and designers had immense problems to overcome in insuring that the priming charges did not fall out of the pans when the cylinder rotated. Great ingenuity was displayed in producing repeating priming systems, which poured fresh charges of powder into each pan as it came to the top and aligned with the barrel, but none of these was consistently reliable, although the Collier revolver of 1818 came close to being ideal. The Collier predated most of the innovations that were credited to other inventors in the next 60 or 70 years, but it never sold in very large numbers mainly because it was heavy and unwieldly, and now only a handful survive in museums.

Pepperbox revolver

The development of a practical revolver became possible when the percussion-cap method of ignition was invented. With percussion caps, the cylinder could be loaded with powder and bullet, primed with caps and carried in the pocket or holster with certainty that each chamber would fire when the trigger was pulled. For simplicity, most of these early percussion revolvers were what is now called the pepperbox type, because each chamber was also its own barrel – an arrangement that resembled a pepper shaker. The pepperbox was easy to make, but it was a clumsy way of carrying more than one shot.

Development of modern types

One man can be said to be the father of the modern revolver – Samuel Colt. His models of 1847 laid the pattern for all subsequent revolvers and since then the multitude of designs that have appeared throughout the world have been little more than variations upon the basic Colt. When the metallic cartridge was invented in the 1860s, it was adapted to revolvers without difficulty and the weapon began a phenomenal wave of popularity.

The modern revolver still closely resembles the original Colt, but there are many improvements, particularly in strength and general resistance to rough treatment. Internally, there are detailed changes, but the principles are the same. There are now two broad divisions of revolver types: the *single-action* and the *double-action*. All early designs were single-action, but today this style is retained only for target weapons or replicas. In the single-action revolver, the hammer has to be pulled

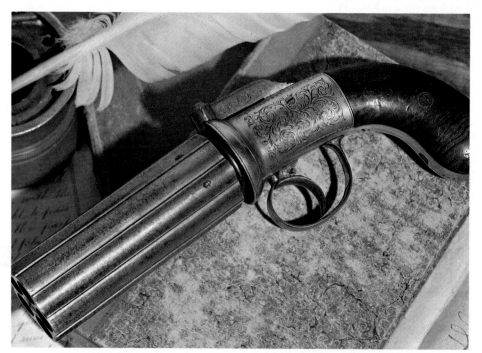

Left: A revolving pepperbox pistol. The design first appeared in the 1780s, each barrel having its own pan and frizzen in the early models. However, it was only with the introduction of percussion ignition that the pepperbox became a practical weapon. In this later example, the hammer is concealed within the butt.

Right: A .357 in. Model 27 Smith and Wesson Magnum with its cylinder open and cartridges being extracted. The first of many models of the Magnum revolver was introduced in 1935, and for several years it was the most powerful handgun available. The barrel is 6 in. (152 mm) long. The rate of fire is 12 rpm. The bullet weight is 0.36 oz (10.22 g) and muzzle velocity 1450 ft/sec (442 m/sec).

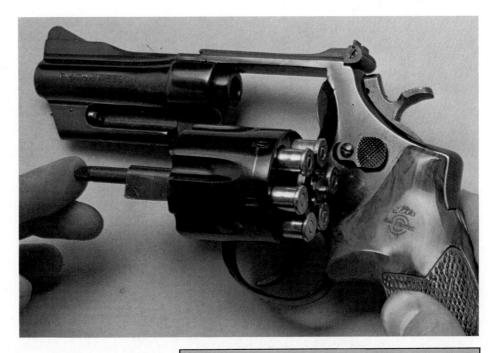

back by the shooter's thumb to cock the hammer and rotate the cylinder around to the next chamber.

In the double-action mechanism, the trigger not only fires the shot, but it also cocks the hammer and rotates the cylinder in the first part of its backward movement. In doing these functions, it usually travels a fairly long way, and the pull is heavy. This long and heavy trigger pull makes the weapon difficult to hold an accurate aim, so the double-action system tends to be used for close-range shooting. Many double systems can act as single-action if the hammer is cocked by the thumb.

These combined mechanisms are extremely ingenious. To fire a chamber, the trigger has to complete several functions in the correct order. It must unlock the cylinder, cock the hammer, rotate the cylinder, lock the cylinder again, release the hammer to fire the cartridge and finally withdraw the hammer slightly so that the cylinder is not jammed by the firing pin. All this is achieved with a few levers and springs in a tiny and irregular space inside the body. A few revolvers have no thumb piece on the hammer, and are meant to be fired double-action at every shot. These are usually special pocket revolvers in which the designer tries to eliminate items that will catch in the firer's clothing.

Nearly all modern revolvers are six-chambered, because this is a suitable number to accommodate the popular sizes of pistol cartridge. Five chambers are often found on small pocket models, and there have been revolvers with up to 12 chambers, but these were impractical freaks. Loading is by one of two methods: either the cylinder drops out to one side on a pivoted arm, or *crane,* or the barrel and cylinder unlock and tilt forward, exposing the back

• FACT FILE •

- The Velo Dog revolver was produced in 1894 in France specifically for use by cyclists to ward off dogs while cycling in the countryside. It employed a 0.2 in. (5.5 mm) cartridge, was short barreled, and had a folding trigger.

- The Bland four-barrel pistol had a rotating firing pin instead of a rotating chamber. Four barrels were fired in succession. It was made in London, England, especially for army officers.

- The Dardick open-chambered pistols, which came onto the market in 1954, have a revolving cylinder that transports ammunition from a box magazine in the butt. The cartridges are roughly triangular in cross section, and known as Trounds. Each firing ejects one Tround and brings up another into the chamber.

of the cylinder and the chambers. With each type an ejector expels the empty cases in one movement and the shooter simply has to push in six fresh ones.

Much ingenuity has been wasted in attempting to close the small gap between the cylinder and barrel which allows some of the propelling gas to escape every time the revolver fires. But the complexity of this has never been found to be worth the effort.

Rear sight · Bullet in chamber · Revolving cylinder · Barrel · Front sight

Hammer (uncocked)

Ratchet

Empty chamber

Hand pivoted on trigger lever

When squeezed, the trigger of a revolver rotates (A) on its axis and is lifted up into contact with the hammer, compressing the main spring. Eventually, the trigger ceases contact (B) with the hammer, which is released and forced by the main spring into contact with the bullet.

Main spring

Cylinder stop
Trigger lever
Trigger

Trigger spring

Hammer

Trigger lever

Frame

Main spring compressed · A · B

Stock

The greatest asset of the revolver is that it is the most reliable repeating weapon ever made. The mechanics are so simple that it is almost impossible for it to jam, and if a cartridge fails to fire, the shooter has merely to continue pulling the trigger and another cartridge will be brought round to the hammer. With an automatic pistol the failure of one cartridge jams the gun.

Other applications
The revolver principle has also been applied to weapons other than pistols. In the days of the first metallic cartridges, there were several revolver rifles but they failed because the rotating cylinder was not suited to firing a powerful cartridge, and other mechanisms were better. In the machine gun, the revolver principle proved to be most suitable. Doctor Gatling grouped a number of barrels around a central axis in the same way as with the pepperbox. He then arranged a simple hand crank to turn the barrels and a cam system to open and close the bolts on each as they rotated.

The U.S. Fairchild A-10 Thunderbolt II ground attack plane carries an immensely powerful modern version of Dr Gatling's original principle. It is called the GAU-8 Gatling and is 21 ft (6 m) long, has seven rotating, externally powered barrels and delivers 30 mm shells at either 2400 or 4800 rounds per minute. The GAU-8 is normally fired in half-second bursts.

The chief rival to the revolver as a hand gun is the automatic pistol. This produces a higher muzzle velocity and a greater volume of fire in a given time because the magazines of automatics can take up to 13 rounds, and a full magazine can be slid in place quickly to replace an empty one. Automatic or self-loading pistols, however, have a complicated mechanism and are more liable to jam, as well as being less accurate than a revolver with single-action firing. For this reason, police forces tend to issue the rugged and reliable revolver, although it is harder to conceal.

See also: Ammunition; Ballistics; Rifle.

Rifle

A rifle is a firearm that imparts a spinning motion to its projectile for greater accuracy. This spinning motion is caused by spiral grooves (rifling) cut into the inner surface of the barrel which engage with the projectile on its way to the muzzle. The rotation so acquired continues during flight, giving *gyroscopic stability* which equalizes the tendencies to erratic flight arising from any irregularities in the shape or density of the projectile.

In general usage, the word rifle has come to mean a shoulder-controlled weapon capable of being carried and used by one person and firing a relatively small-size high-velocity bullet.

Before the invention of gunpowder, projectiles – such as arrows – were usually fin-stabilized in flight. Indeed the spin-stabilization of rifling is normally ineffective for long, thin projectiles and much more effective for short, fat ones. This fact can be demonstrated easily by spinning a top and a pencil. The top will be quite hard to pull out of line but a pencil would have to spin on its end at incredible speeds to stay upright. With the advent of short, fat projectiles fired from guns, rifling became worthwhile. Short, fat projectiles, however, do not penetrate as easily as long, thin ones made of dense material, so smooth-bore guns which fire fin-stabilized projectiles have recently become popular once more in the antitank role.

Rifles were used mainly for sport, though small numbers were introduced into all armies. These rifles were all *muzzle loaders* and the drawback to the muzzle-loading rifle lay in the difficulty of getting the ball to fit the rifling, and of clearing the rifling grooves of powder fouling. Most muzzle loaders used a tight-fitting bullet, which was rammed or even hammered down the barrel, an operation which took much time and was acceptable for game shooting, but not in war.

The *breech-loading* systems, which were invented in the 1860s, changed the whole aspect of rifling. The bullet no longer had to be forced down the barrel, because it could now be introduced to the rifling at its beginning, just in front of the breech. Soon bullets became cylindrical in shape and more efficient, and with the invention of high-pressure powders at the end of the nineteenth century, the final form of the rifle was completed.

Right: Some of the best shots in the world enjoy the sport of target shooting, but even the best target shooter is unlikely ever to put ten bullets through the same bullet hole in the center of a target. The shooter on the left is using a sling to support his arm, and a stiff glove to strengthen his hand. The man on the right is using a palm rest. Target shooting is a popular sport, requiring the greatest coordination and judgement, and the finest weapons ever made are the tools of the sport.

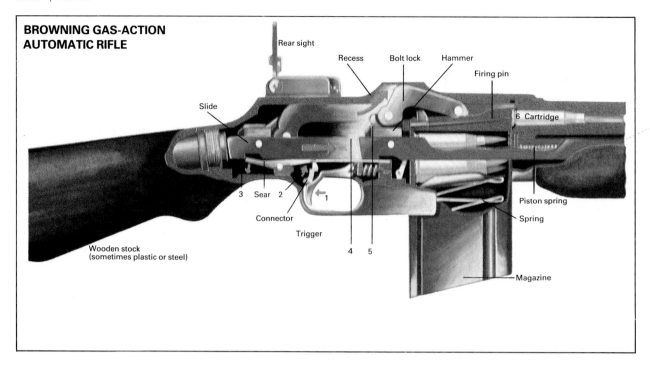

BROWNING GAS-ACTION AUTOMATIC RIFLE

Rear sight

Recess   Bolt lock   Hammer

Firing pin

Slide

6 Cartridge

3   Sear   2   ←1

Connector

Trigger

Piston spring

Spring

4   5

Wooden stock
(sometimes plastic or steel)

Magazine

Above: The Browning gas-action automatic rifle reloads itself, allowing a much higher rate of fire than a simple repeater. When the trigger is squeezed (1), it raises the connector, which then raises the sear (2) and depresses the end of the sear, disengaging the slide (3). Under tension from the piston spring, the slide moves forward (4) and the bolt lock is forced up into the locked position. The slide, still moving forward (5), brings the hammer into contact with the firing pin which strikes the cartridge (6). The bullet passes the gas port (7), allowing pressure in the barrel to force back the piston. The slide now recoils, unlocking the bolt lock. Meanwhile, the cartridge is withdrawn by an extractor in the bolt mechanism and discarded. The recoil helps to operate the mechanism, so the rifle is comfortable to use.

Bolt-action rifles

Rifles have changed little in the last 70 years. The only significant innovations have been the self-loading systems and even smaller calibers. All the older rifles were hand-operated and they used a diversity of mechanisms, some of which have survived today. By far the most practical mechanism, and also one of the earliest to be used, is the bolt action. With this type of action the breech is closed by a device similar to the domestic barrel bolt found on household doors. The rifle bolt has a small hole drilled through its length to accommodate the firing pin. The action is arranged so that on opening the bolt the firing pin is withdrawn and cocked, ready for the next shot.

The first bolt-action rifles were *single-shot*, each cartridge having to be put into the bolt-way and the empty case pulled out and discarded. It was not long before *repeating rifles* were made, in which there was a magazine of several rounds of ammunition and a system of feeding the rounds successively into the breech. Enormous ingenuity was displayed in the design of repeaters, but the bolt system has proved to be the best and simplest for general use. A magazine is placed below the bolt and the rounds are pressed upward by a spring. As the bolt is pushed forward by the shooter, it strips a cartridge off the top of the magazine and runs it into the breech. An extractor pulls out the empty case. Speed of firing depends on how fast the bolt is operated.

Bolt action rifles are used in large numbers for sporting and target shooting, and a few are retained by armies for sniping. Practically all these rifles are of a similar size and weight, being about 10 lb (4.5 kg) together with ammunition, and they all shoot bullets of about 0.30 in. (8 mm) caliber. A rifle of this type can fire a bullet to a range of more than 6000 ft (1800 m) and will be capable of hitting a target 2 ft (0.6 m) square at half a mile (0.8 km).

Self-loaders

Normal military rifles are no longer hand-operated and all use some type of self-loading system which requires the firer only to pull the trigger. The mechanism is operated by the force of recoil or, more usually, the gas generated by the propellant powder. The firer has only to take a fresh aim and pull the trigger after each shot, and so can shoot far more rapidly for less effort than with a hand-operated rifle, because the firer's hand need not be taken off

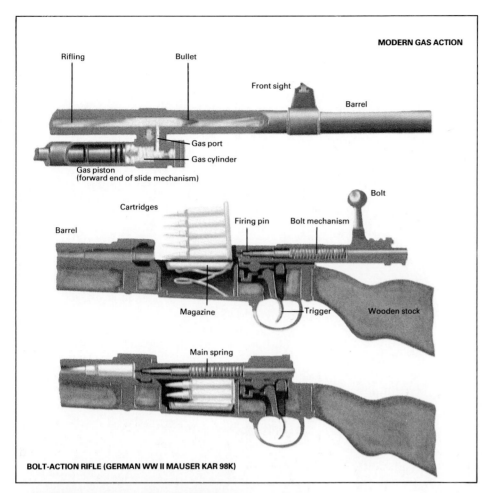

MODERN GAS ACTION

Rifling
Bullet
Front sight
Barrel
Gas port
Gas cylinder
Gas piston
(forward end of slide mechanism)

Cartridges
Bolt
Barrel
Firing pin
Bolt mechanism
Magazine
Trigger
Wooden stock

Main spring

BOLT-ACTION RIFLE (GERMAN WW II MAUSER KAR 98K)

Left: A bolt-action rifle. The first bolt action rifles were single-shot, but now many incorporate magazines holding several rounds of ammunition, as the one shown here. The rifle is unlocked by turning the bolt handle up and pulling back the bolt mechanism. The cartridges are dropped into the magazine. When the bolt is pushed home it chambers the top cartridge and cocks the piece. When the trigger is squeezed, the main spring is released and forces the firing pin against the cartridge. When the bolt is retracted, the cartridge is ejected automatically.

Above: This soldier's rifle is fitted with a laser, so when in training he scores a hit on an enemy, it deactivates his rifle. The system enables soldiers to be efficiently trained to high standards, without having to fire expensive ammunition.

one part to operate another. Self-loading systems are more complicated and more expensive but for military needs the inconvenience is worthwhile.

There is a general move in modern military rifles toward smaller calibers and lighter weapons. The present U.S. army rifle is a 0.223 in. (5.56 mm) caliber. In using a lighter, smaller-caliber round, the U.S. Army has begun a virtual revolution in military rifle design. It has been discovered that infantry rarely engage targets at more than 1000 ft (300 m) in battle and this range can be attained by a smaller, lighter bullet fired from a lighter rifle.

The lighter the bullet, the higher must its velocity be for it to be effective. Yet there are great gains in lightness because the infantry trooper is always overburdened, so there have been experiments with rifles of an even smaller caliber. The German firm, Heckler and Koch, have produced the HK 36 Experimental rifle which fires a 4.6 mm round in controlled bursts of three to give a higher hit probability. Unfortunately, bullets as small as that tend to produce excessive wear in the barrel. Research is continuing into ways of overcoming this problem.

See also: Automatic weapon; Gun; Revolver.

The ultimate rifle

It is not easy to take seriously – it seems to be made entirely out of plastic – and the bullets it fires are smaller than air rifle slugs. The bullets do not even have cartridge cases, but this is no child's toy. The Heckler & Koch G11 rifle is deadly. Bullets leave the barrel at 3000 ft/s (930 m/s) – and in such quick succession that the third has left the barrel before the recoil of the first is felt. The bullets will go straight through the steel helmet of an enemy 1960 ft (600 m) away. The rifle and ammunition are so light that you can carry six times as many bullets as an enemy using a typical NATO 7.62 mm rifle.

The West German Army, the Bundeswehr, is to adopt this rifle. The reasons behind the choice make an interesting illustration of how battle tactics and logistics can influence weapon design.

In the late 1960s, the Bundeswehr began thinking about their next generation of small arms, and in a remarkable burst of openmindedness circulated manufacturers with an unusual invitation. Provided the weapon met the standard requirements regarding range, reliability and accuracy, they would be prepared to accept any design, however outlandish, on condition that it would guarantee to place a three-shot burst with an accuracy of 1.2 to 2 mils.

One mil is one-thousandth of any given range, so that three shots would have to fall within a 2 to 3 ft (0.6 to 1 m) circle at 1640 ft (500 m) range.

This sort of accuracy is impossible with a conventional type of rifle or machine gun, because the recoil force after each shot lifts the barrel and disturbs the aim, so that successive shots are spread around. If a gun could be developed to fire at, say, 2500 rounds a minute, then it might be possible, because the three shots would follow each other very closely, before the recoil had moved the barrel. The mechanical problems were excessive, and anyway, nobody wants a weapon that regularly fires at such a speed.

Heckler & Koch, the German weapons manufacturer, came to the conclusion that demand required a rifle with a gentle recoil (so as not to throw it off target), a flat trajectory and high velocity (to reduce the time of flight of the bullet), and a rate of fire in excess of 2000 rounds per minute for the three-round burst. All this demanded a totally new approach to the mechanism. The first major decision was to adopt a caseless cartridge, a round of ammunition that dispensed with the conventional brass or steel cartridge case. This would lighten the soldier's load, and it would also simplify the design of the weapon, because it would no longer have to mechanically extract and eject the empty case after each shot. Heckler & Koch collaborated with Dynamit Nobel, a firm with generations of experi-

Left: A German soldier using a Heckler and Koch G11 quick-firing rifle. The burst fire capability gives a wide spread of bullets and improves the chances of hitting a target by 90 per cent. The bullets are smaller than air rifle slugs and are shot from the weapon so quickly that three bullets leave before the recoil of the first is felt.

ence in ammunition design, to develop a caseless round with a 4.7 mm bullet. This bullet is embedded in a solid block of propellant explosive, a percussion cap being embedded in the other end.

With the caseless cartridge in hand, the next problem was to design a rifle to fire it. It was soon apparent that conventional rifle mechanisms were simply not suitable and that something new would have to be devised.

The full details of the mechanism are still secret, but enough has been revealed to permit an understanding of the basic principle of operation. The heart of the weapon is an unusual rotating breech block which contains the firing chamber. This is a metal drum, bored to accept the cartridge, which rotates behind the rifle barrel. In the firing position the chamber is in line with the barrel: to reload, the drum turns through 90° so that the chamber is vertical and a fresh cartridge can drop in.

The entire mechanism – barrel, breech, magazine, gas system and all – is concealed inside a futuristic reinforced plastic housing. This is shaped to form the butt and pistol grip and also to form a carrying handle which conceals an optical sight. The magazine, a long box containing 50 cartridges, is inserted horizontally above the barrel, so that the cartridges feed downward into the breech. Except for the muzzle, there are no apertures which will allow water or dust to enter the weapon, the trigger and magazine being sealed by rubber flanges. The sight is provided with battery-illuminated cross wires for firing in poor light.

On firing, the entire mechanism, including the magazine, recoils inside the plastic housing against a spring, so that the recoil felt by the firer is more like a gentle push than a sharp blow. The chamber revolves and is reloaded during the recoil movement and the rifle is ready to fire again immediately. A change lever above the trigger permits selection of either single shots, three-round bursts, continuous automatic fire, or a safe position. On changing to three-round bursts, the unique nature of this weapon becomes apparent.

During the recoil stroke the breech rotates and loads a second round, which is immediately fired and the recoil force of the second shot adds to the movement of the mechanism. Now the breech rotates again, reloads, and fires the third shot of the burst; once more the recoil force adds to the movement, and at last the mechanism is permitted to complete its rearward stroke, and return to the ready position. The recoil movement within the plastic casing is about three times as much as that of a single shot, but due to the buffering the force felt by the firer is still relatively mild. The important

THE G11 OPERATING PRINCIPLE

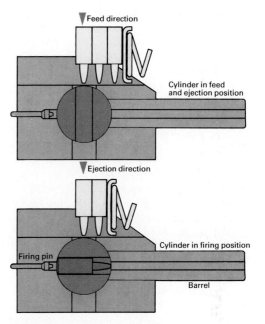

Above: The G11 rifle operates by a rotating bolt, which moves much faster than a conventional rifle bolt. The mechanism loads and fires three rounds in only 0.075 seconds.

thing, however, is that all three shots leave the barrel before the firer feels the recoil shock and before the barrel begins to move off target. So the three shots fly close together and strike the target well within the designated spread. A single shot fired in combat by an average soldier has, perhaps, a 50 per cent chance of hitting the target, depending on factors such as wind strength. Three shots fired rapidly and with a small spread improve the chance of hitting to about 90 per cent.

The development program is scheduled to be completed in 1987. The Bundeswehr has committed itself to adopting the G11 in 1990, a date arrived at purely on financial grounds and open to adjustment. But other NATO armies have expressed interest in the G11 and its ammunition, and it is not impossible that there could be co-production agreements and that the rifle could go into service with some other NATO army before 1990.

The concept of the caseless cartridge is a tough pill to swallow for many conventionally minded experts. There are potential storage and safety hazards to be considered; there will be vast changes in national ammunition manufacturing capacity. But the weapon of tomorrow is here today, and rifle design will never be quite the same.

Riot control

Shooting demonstrators is a speedy way of ending a riot, but to do so is normally unacceptable, and will inflame an angry gathering. A more civilized answer to civil disturbance is to use riot equipment to control, rather than crush, a crowd.

Since the 1960s and 1970s many governments have had to confront the problem of sustained riots in city areas. The army, National Guard, and police, however, can no longer consider the sort of tactics that were developed by the British Army during their long history of dealing with colonial troubles. Among these was the calculated use of guns against a rioting march. The crowd would be confronted by a line of soldiers with banners and loudspeakers warning them that if they crossed a white tape on the ground they would be shot. A sniper was in position, and when the first person crossed the tape he or she was shot.

Below: French CRS riot police, equipped with shields, helmets, and truncheons, prepare to meet demonstrators. CS gas and rubber bullets are standard equipment for riot-control police today.

Such uses of firearms escalate the level of violence. Although a single shot fired at one person may seem discriminating, it can pass through and wound an innocent member of the public – and because the round has been distorted, the wounds from ricochets are more severe than those from a medium-range direct hit.

High pressure

One of the first riot control techniques to be developed as an alternative to the use of firearms was the use of high-pressure water. For example, Civil Rights marchers in the southern states of the U.S. were drenched by the local fire department. High-pressure hoses can be used to knock people over, and bowl them along the street. Firefighters, however, have no protection if the crowd decides to retaliate by throwing rocks. The water cannon – an armored truck, with high-pressure hoses aimed from turrets – has been used in European riots. The water can be used with vegetable dye, which turns rioters green or blue, making subsequent follow-up and arrest easier for the security forces. CS or CN gas (often referred to incorrectly as tear gas) can be added to the water to make it additionally effective. Water cannons have a major disadvantage, however,

RIOT CONTROL HARDWARE

Above and right: The .38 Special Mighty Midget grenade launcher fires a pocket-sized military grenade (1). The Tru-Flite TM 37 mm Penetrating Projectile fires a fin-stabilized rubber projectile (2). The Smith and Wesson rubber-ball grenade (3) eliminates the possibility of throwback. A Mace spray (4) blinds demonstrators temporarily. The Military Type Continuous Discharge grenade (5) is a crowd-control grenade which can emit either CS or CN gas or smoke. Designed to be hand-thrown, the grenade has a military-type safety pin.

they can, and often do, run out of water.

Water cannons are also not freely mobile. During the 1985 riots in the London Borough of Tottenham, the rioters were able to retreat from the police and regroup in the warren of stairways and landings that lay within nearby tower-block housing. At the time, the police had neither water cannons nor plastic bullets available but, if this had not been so, they would have found the water cannon ineffective and the plastic bullets invaluable for following up the fleeing mob. Although 100 ft (30 m) is the minimum range recommended for firing plastic bullets, they are frequently used at far less distances and are sometimes fatal.

The British Army went to Northern Ireland in 1969 with three weapons in their riot-control armory – clubs, shields and CS smoke. The shields were metal (in Cyprus the British Army had used wicker shields, but they were not strong enough to withstand a steady battering of bricks).

From police experience of the Hong Kong riots in the 1960s came the idea of the baton round. In the Far East this had taken the form of a wooden rod fired from a riot gun. It hit the ground just short of the rioters, and then bounced into their ranks, at about knee height. In Northern Ireland, and subsequently in other countries, it has been refined. The rubber bullet version, introduced in 1970, is about 6 in. (152 mm) long, 1.5 in. (38 mm) in

diameter, and weighs 5 oz (141 g). It is superior to the wooden round because it does not splinter.

Rubber bullets were not absolutely satisfactory, however, and the British authorities carried out an investigation of the effects made by 33,000 rubber batons fired in Northern Ireland between 1970 and 1972. A mortality rate of 1:16,000 was considered acceptable but a disability rate of 1:1900 and a serious injury rate of 1:800 were too great. As a result, an improved plastic round (L3A1 & L5A2) was introduced in 1972.

This new plastic round turned out to be 0.5 oz (13 g) lighter, but only marginally less dangerous than its rubber predecessor. Its advantage from a riot-control point of view is that it is much more accurate and, in its long-range version, can outrange a stone thrower. It proved, with certain other measures, to be the magic wand with which British security forces asserted control over rioting crowds in Northern Ireland.

Baton rounds are fired from weapons such as the Schermuly 1.5 in. Multi-Purpose Gun, or the Smith and Wesson Grenade Laucher. These single-shot weapons are like short-shot guns, and can fire several types of ammunition. Beside dispatching rubber bullets, they can be used to fire rounds of CS smoke. The rounds have a range of 330 ft (100 m) and a burning time of ten to 25 seconds. The launcher is, therefore, an effective weapon that can

flush terrorists out from a building. It was used in the British SAS operation against the Iranian Embassy in London in 1980. Unless a number of CS rounds are fired, however, the launcher is not effective for controlling crowds in the open.

CS dangers

CS is a nonlethal irritant. It can however, cause harm to people with respiratory problems – if those people are confined in a small area and exposed to a high concentration of the irritant. In the open, it makes its victims feel as if they have been attacked with pepper – the eyes and mouth sting, and the nose runs. Exposure to the thick clouds of the smoke leads to coughing, or even vomiting. The smoke also irritates the skin.

CS has its limitations. For example, security forces in the U.S. found that rioters are prepared to grab the grenade after it has landed, and then throw it back. In Northern Ireland, rioters discovered that they could defeat CS by creating a mask from a wet handkerchief wrapped around the nose and mouth. And because the CS smoke forms a visible gray cloud it can be avoided.

One answer to the unplanned return of grenades is a version designed to split up like a high explosive. For riot control, the grenade body has to be nonmetallic, or the explosion would cause perma-

nent injury. The L13A1/L16A1 grenade has a rubber body which ruptures when a small ignition charge explodes. This charge also spreads 23 CS pellets over an area of 270 to 380 sq ft (25 to 35 sq m). The pellets burn for only eight to nine seconds, but the CS cloud hangs for a longer period in still air.

A problem with hand-thrown grenades is that the range is limited by the ability of the thrower to pitch them at the crowd. Launchers allow security forces to fire CS canisters at greater distance over the heads of the crowd. The launchers can be fitted to rifles, or grouped in a battery on riot-control vehicles. The Paris riots of 1968 saw the special riot squad (the CRS) firing smoke grenades directly at the crowd, and then following up with truncheons.

CS can also be sprayed from hand-held aerosols. This form is particularly potent because the victim receives a concentrated dose of CS at a range of 5 ft (1.5 m). It will subdue the most violent person. The U.S. police forces carry a Mace spray as part of their individual kit. About 400,000 Mace weapons are in service with 4000 police departments in the U.S.

Pepper fog

At the other end of the scale is the Smith and Wesson Pepper Fog Tear Smoke generator. This machine can pump out CS or CN smoke to cover thousands of cubic feet, for up to 45 minutes.

Beside CS smoke and rubber bullets, there are some more exotic weapons in the armory of the security forces. The Bean Bag is a round fired from a riot gun. It consists of a bag delivering the impact of a boxer's punch, but once the energy of the bag is expended the bag is hard to throw back. The Ring Airfoil Grenade (RAG) is another U.S. idea. It consists of a rubber ring about the size of a large napkin ring which can be aimed accurately up to 160 ft (50 m).

Riot control can be more effective if the police are less obvious. For example, the Shorland armored vehicles (developed in Northern Ireland) have become a successful British export. They are less conspicuous than other armored vehicles, and being based on the conventional Land Rover, they are easy to drive. Ventilation allows the crew and passengers to stay safely enclosed, even in hot weather.

They move fast and are more effective in urban areas than tracked vehicles, such as tanks or Armored Personnel Carriers. Tanks are intimidating by their sheer bulk and noise, but, as Russian commanders discovered in Budapest in 1956, battle tanks are unwieldly in town streets.

Armor at the barricades?

Specialized armored vehicles normally have a boat-shaped hull, searchlights, loudspeakers, armored glass for vision ports, and the facility to mount a machine gun. Some have dozer blades at the front for clearing the barricades. They serve as a troop carrier and as an offensive vehicle. Police forces have also used armored vehicles for operations involving armed criminals.

France and Switzerland have produced several types of vehicles, but the British have either adapted the Land Rover or used standard military

Left: Police using a Smith and Wesson Pepper fog tear-smoke generator to disgroup rioters in Berkley, California.
Right: The Soviet method of clearing a city square, using tanks. The demonstrators are herded out of the square by sealing one side of the area, and driving a line of tanks toward the other side, where several outlets have been deliberately left open by the troops. After the square has been cleared the troops push forward down the outlet streets, and close them off to prevent people from returning.

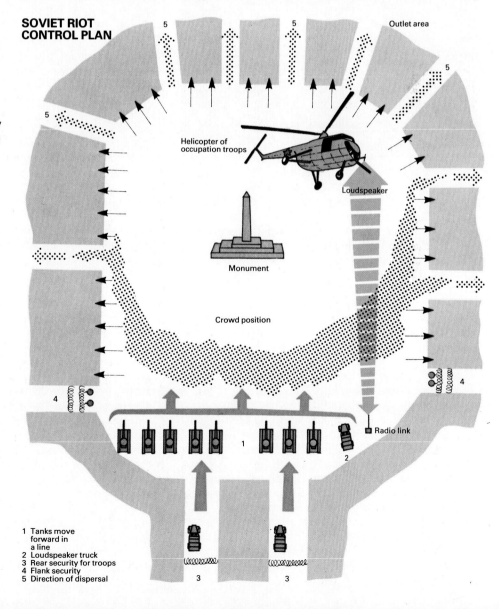

SOVIET RIOT CONTROL PLAN

Outlet area

Helicopter of occupation troops

Loudspeaker

Monument

Crowd position

Radio link

1 Tanks move forward in a line
2 Loudspeaker truck
3 Rear security for troops
4 Flank security
5 Direction of dispersal

Above: Police equipped with riot shields attempt to halt protestors marching through London, England; their main aim is to insure that the peaceful demonstration does not turn into a riot.

machines, such as the Alvis Saladin armored car, the Alvis Saracen APC, and the Daimler Ferret Scout Car. The one-ton Humber APC, known universally as the Pig, has been used by every regiment that has served in Northern Ireland.

In South Africa the police operate from Hippos – 4-ton trucks which have the cab and seats mounted above the chassis. The Hippo is, therefore, mineproof and puts its occupants nearly 10 ft (3 m) above the ground where they can see clearly.

One of the most significant materials used for protecting troops and police is makrolon polycarbonate – a clear, tough plastic material first developed for astronauts' visors. When fitted as a protective helmet, it can withstand rocks thrown at short range, and though it may crack after a sustained assault, it does not shatter. After visors, two types of shield were introduced in Northern Ireland, and those have become more widely available to police forces. The small shield is useful for mobile groups, while the 5 ft (1.5 m) shield gives excellent protection to troops who have to form a cordon separating rival groups or stone-throwing youths.

The flak jacket is an important part of most internal security operations where a crowd is likely to be used as cover for a sniper. The normal jacket has about 16 plies of textile sewn together with plastic armor sheeting so that it is flexible.

British security forces have employed the snatch-squad method of securing prisoners for a number of years but today there is more flexibility in the way they are used. In the early 1970s, lines of helmeted, shield-carrying soldiers would absorb hours of attack from hostile stone-throwers and Molotov-cocktail bombers maneuvering like ancient Roman legionaries under fire until the rioters were tempted too close. At that moment the lightly armed snatch squads would burst from their front rank and try to make arrests. This was usually ineffective because the fleetest soldier in boots and helmet cannot afford to give a 100 ft start to fit youths in jeans and training shoes. Since those days, British tactics have become more aggressive and it is now usual for armored vehicles to race up to the fringe of a rioting crowd before disgorging snatch squads and more heavily protected men carrying shield, rifles, riot guns and rubber bullets.

Metal plates

Some jackets can be fitted with metal plates that give greater protection against high-velocity rounds, but they are normally worn by static units. Most protective clothing will only stop pistol rounds or fragments from home-made bombs.

Human inventiveness has reached some extremes in riot control, and a substance known as Instant Banana Peel is one of the more bizarre measures on the market. In the form of a spray, it makes the ground slippery, but it may hinder the police as much as the rioters. Foam is another hindrance – on the theory that no one would want to push through a thick mass of bubbles.

Devices to control crowds without violence are of little concern to the less-sophisticated police and security forces of the world. They favor the use of firearms in riots – even though firing over the crowds is potentially dangerous, because the bullets can hit people in buildings.

The ideal way to end a riot is to disperse it peacefully, and the use of a sedative gas would enable a police force to calm a hostile crowd. A novel by Aldous Huxley, Brave New World, predicted the scene as gas was pumped over a minor disturbance and the rioters were told by a firm but friendly voice that they should return to their work. The use of taped music and announcements has already brought this fantasy a step closer.

See also: Ammunition; Armor; Bomb disposal unit; Bullet; Gas mask; Grenade; Machine gun; Nonlethal weapon; Protective clothing; Rifle.

Riveting

In engineering work, there are permanent and temporary methods of joining together parts of a structure. Screws, keys and pins are examples of temporary fastenings; examples of permanent fastening are welding, brazing, soldering, and riveting.

A rivet consists of a formed head and a cylindrical body or shank. Rivets are usually made of mild steel or, for aircraft construction, of a light alloy. Bridges, roofs, cranes, steel-framed buildings and other such constructions are built of structural members arranged in triangulated forms and secured together by means of rivets. Holes are drilled through two adjacent surfaces, the rivet is inserted, and the shank end of the rivet is hammered flat.

Members of structures which resist tension are called *ties* and those which resist compression are called *struts*. The rivets used in such constructions are subject to *shearing* between the members; the edges of the metal plates act as the blades of shears as the structure is stressed. The spacing of rivets and the number of rows of rivets are determined by the engineers, according to the amount of stress expected. The distance between rivets is the *pitch* and the distance between rivets in adjacent rows is called *diagonal pitch*.

The rivet is said to be under a *single shear stress*. One method of reducing shear stress is the construction of a sandwich of one plate between two plates stressed in opposite directions; the intensity of the stress is cut in half, making the joint twice as strong. The ratio of the strength of the riveted joint to the strength of the solid plate is called the *efficiency* of the joint. A *structural* joint is subject to the load put on the structure; a *boiler* joint is subject to an additional load, which is pressure.

Types of rivets

The head of the rivet may be round (a *snap* head), flat (*pan* head) or countersunk. Snap heads are usually used in machine riveting, while pan heads are hand-hammered in enclosed spaces. Countersunk rivets are used on ships and aircraft to result in a flush surface for decreased resistance against wind or water. The shank of the rivet may be solid or tubular; the part of the shank immediately underneath the head may be tapered to provide a more gradual cross-sectional transition to the head, affording greater resistance against failure.

The part of the rivet farthest from the head is called the *tail*; this is the part which will be hammered or *swaged* by the riveter, while the head is held by the riveter's mate in a *dolly* serving as an anvil. Tubular rivets have the tail splayed into a countersunk hole, or the tail made to bulge into a barrel shape. Some tubular rivets contain small

Above: The Chobert repetition riveting system, introduced in 1932, is now used in many industries. Below: A riveter for home use. The rivet (top) is supplied with a large-headed nail or mandrel.

RIVET GUN

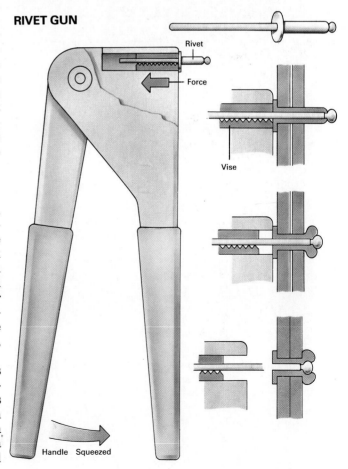

Above: A pneumatic precision riveter being used to anchor an aircraft windshield to the body.
Below: A threaded rivet being compressed. The head is formed by tightening a nut, so there is no need for either heating or hammering.

explosive charges which are set off by heat or a detonating device which forms the rivet head by expansion of the hollow tail.

The hammering may be done by hand or by pneumatic tool. *Squeeze* riveting displaces the metal by means of constant pressure rather than repeated blows. Squeeze riveting is also used with tubular rivets with a mandrel; a hand tool pulls the mandrel through the hollow center to form the opposite head before snapping the mandrel off and releasing the tool. Solid steel rivets of up to 1.2 in. (35 mm) diameter can be headed by a combination of squeezing and radial spinning of the tail end. The tool moves in an orbit and applies a line of pressure from the center outward, displacing some metal with each turn.

Bifurcated rivets, which have a forked tail opened out by hammering, are used for joining leather.

Preparing the work

Riveted joints may be *butt* or *lap* joints. In a lap joint, the plates to be joined are overlapped; in a butt joint they are placed end to end and the area of the joint is covered by additional plates or straps, which should be at least half the thickness of the plate being joined.

The holes are drilled to suit the rivet diameter and the edges of the holes are cleaned of burrs by light countersinking. In precision work, the structure to be joined is screwed or lightly welded (*tacked*) to prevent misalignment, and holes of minimal size are drilled through all components at once.

Rivets are driven home hot. When they cool, they shrink lengthwise, providing a tight joint, but they also shrink away from the walls of the hole, producing an air space for possible leakage. On certain kinds of work such as water tanks and steam boilers, the rivet heads and plate joints must be carefully finished to avoid leaks. *Calking* tools are used. The calking tool resembles a cold chisel and is used in a similar way, except the purpose is to displace metal around edges rather than to cut it. When the tool is about equal in thickness to that of the plate it is called a *fullering* tool.

Testing

Rivets are tested by some of each batch being selected for statistical sampling. To conform to the standards specification, for example, they must withstand a *cold-bending* test of the shank and a *hot-flattening* test of the head. In cold bending, the shank is bent back upon itself and no cracks should appear. In hot flattening, the head is hammered flat to two and a half times the shank diameter with no cracks appearing at the edges.

See also: Alloy; Brazing; Metal; Soldering; Steel manufacture; Welding.

Road construction

Although many early civilizations built roads, it was the Romans who were the first great road builders. Designed for the speedy movement of troops, the roads were built to high standards so that some examples, including bridged sections, are still in existence. In addition, many Roman routes have been followed by modern roads. Following the decline and fall of the Roman Empire, however, much of the road system was allowed to fall into disrepair. Throughout the Middle Ages in Europe, the packhorse was the main means of land transportation and little road building was undertaken.

Elizabeth I of England made it one of the duties of the Justices of the Peace to insure that the local roads were kept in repair. Later, turnpike trusts were set up to maintain the roads and charged tolls on travelers. In 1716, the French king took over responsibility for maintaining his country's roads. Men of ability then began to take an interest in road building. Trésaguet (1716–96) in France and later, toward the end of the eighteenth century, Thomas Telford (1775–1834) and John McAdam (1756–1836) in Britain applied scientific principles to road construction.

Road building in France and Europe was encouraged by Napoleon, who required good, direct roads to move his armies. Several roads over the Alps were then built. These improved roads produced the heyday of the stagecoach, but the advent of the railways in the 1830s stopped this road building.

Early in the twentieth century, the development of motorized transportation required the improvement of road surfaces using tarmacadam (black top), but World War I delayed a further phase of great road building. Between the World Wars, the growth of the U.S. automobile industry produced a quickened pace of road building, and in Germany the *Autobahnen* formed the first national express highway system.

Road design

Traffic planning is the first stage in the design of a new highway, long-range forecasts being made of the traffic requirements for the region concerned. These forecasts have to take into account factors such as the probable increases in traffic flow, the volume and type of existing flows and the nature of the country to be crossed. Consideration also has to be given to the way finance will be raised for construction. Once the highway authority has decided to construct a new major road, it will employ either its own engineers or a consulting engineer to survey the alternate routes and carry out the road design. Information is required, for each of the possible routes, about the detailed ground levels of the ter-

Above: This type of interchange to link freeways is a familiar sight in the developed world. Often, the interchange is constructed while traffic continues to use neighboring roads, and accurate planning is necessary to keep disruptions to a minimum.

rain, which can now be obtained by aerial photography which is accurate to 6 in. (152 mm). Details of the types of material for the construction of embankments, and of the geological strata, must be obtained from *trial pits* and *bore holes* taken along the line of the route and at bridge sites. The local climatic conditions, such as fog, frost and rain, must also be established. In developed countries information is required about land values and various environmental factors which may involve public inquiries in addition to consultation with interested parties. The question of environmental impact has become increasingly important with modern highway schemes with special measures being taken in sensitive areas. For example, the highway may be hidden from sight by running it through a cutting, or the design modified to reduce the effects of noise.

From the survey information, the line and level of each of the possible roads will be chosen in accordance with the standards of gradient, sight lines and other factors laid down by the traffic authority. This should minimize the amount of material that has to be excavated and carried to fill the adjacent

Above: A jackhammer being used to break up rock to prepare the foundations for a new freeway.
Below: A typical composite construction black-top highway usually consists of these four layers.

ROAD STRUCTURE

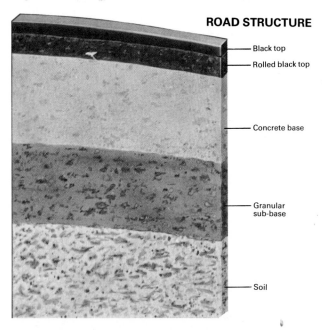

- Black top
- Rolled black top
- Concrete base
- Granular sub-base
- Soil

embankments. It is also important to keep to a minimum the size of the bridges needed to cross railways, rivers and other roads. Taking into account these various factors, the choice of route is made and the design carried out.

Arrangements are then made to purchase the land on which the road will run. Detailed drawings, specifications and estimations of cost are prepared so that contractors can bid, normally in competition with each other, for the construction of the work. The consulting engineer or highway authority will usually provide a resident engineer and site staff to insure that the work is carried out by the successful contractor in accordance with the drawings and specifications. Within the requirements of the design, the contractor will be responsible for deciding upon the methods of construction to be used, including the design of temporary works, and will also be responsible for formulating a program of order and speed of work.

Site preparation

The route of the new road is staked out, cleared and fenced where necessary. Trees are cut down, stumps and roots are grabbed up by crawler dozers or, where necessary, blasted out by explosives. It may also be necessary to build temporary haul roads and bridges or fords at the site of the river bridges.

The bases of embankments and the slopes of cuttings must be protected from the action of ground water which could cause them to collapse. A primary drainage system is therefore constructed before starting earthworks along the length of the road to cut off the natural ground drainage, and prevent it from entering the works. This is usually done by digging a shallow *cut-off ditch* with a hydraulic excavator which has a shaped bucket. At the low point of the natural ground, the water flowing in these ditches is taken across the road line in piped or reinforced-concrete *culverts* and allowed to flow away through the existing streams or ditches. If the ground underneath the new embankments is weak and waterlogged, *band drains* are laid before the embankments are placed to alleviate subsidence after the road is opened.

Earthworks

The topsoil is first stripped and stacked for spreading on the slopes of cuttings and embankments toward the end of construction. This work is usually done with caterpillar tractors towing *box scrapers*. The main cutting and embankment work is then started, using rubber-tired scrapers. These are single- or twin-engined machines which have a horizontal blade that can be lowered to cut a slice of earth from the ground and collect this earth in the bowl of the scraper. When the scraper bowl is full — some machines can carry up to 100 cu yd (75 cu m) —

The BK95 paver is essentially a system of conveyers that receives black top from dumper trucks and extrudes it in the desired width or thickness on a prepared surface. The machine is fitted with heaters, so the black top remains workable until it is rolled. The hopper has a capacity of 13 tons, so it can pave continuously between refills.

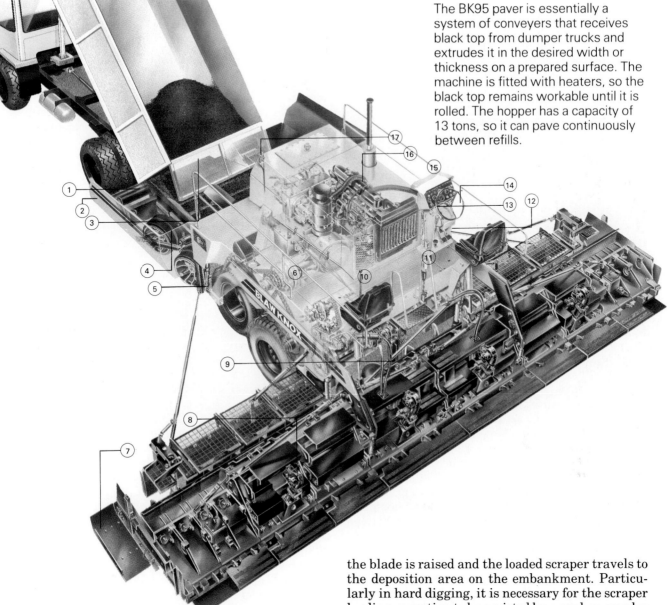

the blade is raised and the loaded scraper travels to the deposition area on the embankment. Particularly in hard digging, it is necessary for the scraper loading operation to be assisted by a pusher crawler which pushes the scraper while it is loading to speed up the operation. For certain types of material, such as chalk which may soften in wet weather, or when the excavated material has to be carried for more than 2 miles (3 km), the excavation may be done using *face shovel* or *back acter* excavators loading into dump trucks. When rock is encountered, this is first shattered with explosives and ripped by the tractor and then loaded by face shovel.

At the embankment, the earth is spread by the scrapers into a thin layer about 12 in. (300 mm) thick which is leveled by dozers and then compacted by caterpillar tractors towing rollers, or by self-propelled rollers. It is essential that the successive embankment layers are properly compacted so that the embankment is stable.

Main features of the BK 95 Paver:
1 Rollers enable contact with wheels
2 Hopper
3 Conveyers with infinitely variable speed control move materials from hopper to rear
4 Steerable wheels
5 Pavement height adjustment
6 Drive-shaft
7 Variable-width screed
8 Black top heaters
9 Hydraulic hoses
10 Transmission lever
11 Heater igniter
12 Foot brakes
13 Throttle
14 Conveyer control
15 Movable console
16 Diesel engine
17 Flow gate gauge

Far left: Grading compacted soil to insure an even surface.
Left: After the soil surface has been graded, the foundation – of varying thickness depending on the expected flow and weight of traffic – is laid.
Below: Placing steel beams on concrete piers for a bridge.

Road drainage

On completion of the earthworks, further shallow drain trenches, about 4 ft (1.2 m) deep, are constructed to keep the top layer of the cutting or embankment free from water, which would weaken it. Pipes are laid in these trenches, which are then filled with gravel. In or adjacent to these trenches are laid further pipes to carry the water collected in road gullies from the finished road surface.

Carriageway construction

It is necessary to phase the bridge construction periods so that the bridges are completed ahead of the paving operations and the existing roads diverted over or through them. Where possible, prefabricated bridge units are employed to reduce site work and construction time. The roadway paving operation then begins by the top layer of earth – the *formation* – being accurately trimmed to a 2 in. (50 mm) tolerance by scrapers or a grader. A grader is a wheeled machine which has a steel blade mounted horizontally between its four wheels. This blade can be accurately raised, lowered or tilted by the driver to cut a precise surface.

If the expected traffic loads are light, the graded soil surface can act as the roadway. For slightly heavier traffic conditions, a loose surfacing of gravel, or a similar material, may be used. In both cases grading is repeated periodically to maintain the profile. Soil stabilization may be carried out by mixing dry cement into the top layer of the earth, damping it and compacting it with rollers. The base produced this way can then be used directly or surfaced with a black-top coating.

Where larger volumes of traffic are involved, a more substantial form of construction is needed to increase the load-bearing capacity. A subbase of gravel or crushed rock is spread over the graded earth surface to a thickness of 12 in. (300 mm) or so (depending on the design load) and compacted. This subbase is then normally covered with a further layer around 5 in. (125 mm) thick which forms the actual base of the road which is then paved with flexible tar or rigid concrete.

Black-top roads

The bitumen and stone are heated and mixed together in a site mixing plant, and brought hot, by truck, to the laying point. The material is then tipped into a paver, which spreads it in succeeding layers of *road base, base course* and *wearing course*. These layers are compacted by road rollers to give a firm surface. The accuracy of each successive layer until the final wearing course (usually of asphalt) provides the accuracy of the finished road surface. The total black-top thickness will be up to 12 in. depending on the traffic load. To improve the skid resistance of the road, bitumen-coated stone chippings are spread over the top surface and rolled into it while it is still hot. This is called a *flexible* construction. For a *composite* construction the road base is constructed of dry, lean concrete instead of bituminous material.

Concrete roads

If the final surface is to be concrete then this will consist of a concrete slab approximately 10 in. (250 mm) thick. The actual thickness will depend upon whether the concrete is reinforced. Joints will be incorporated in this slab at about 15 ft (4.6 m) intervals to enable expansion and contraction of the concrete to take place.

Conventionally, the concrete is laid between temporary steel *road forms,* which support the edge of the concrete slab, by a *concrete train.* This consists

of a series of machines which run on rails supported on the road forms. The forms and thus the rails are accurately laid to level well ahead of the train and provide the *level control* for the finished road surface. The first machine in the train is a *placer spreader* which puts the concrete, transported by truck from the concrete mixing plant, between the road forms. The concrete is then compacted and trimmed to true level by successive machines. To provide a skid-resistant surface, the wet concrete is then lightly brushed or otherwise grooved to a shallow depth. Pockets for reflectors are also formed in the wet concrete at this stage.

Recently, *slip-form* machines have been developed, and by using these machines to form the concrete slab, it is possible to eliminate the lengthy process of accurately laying out road forms. These slip-form pavers incorporate traveling side forms within the body of the machine. The degree of vibration compacting the concrete is much greater than with the conventional train so that after the moving forms – approximately 15 ft (4.6 m) long – have slipped past, the fresh concrete is able to stand up without further support. The surface level of the finished concrete is formed by the same machine which is controlled, both for level and direction, by means of electronic or hydraulic *sensor controls* which follow string lines placed at each side of the machine along the roadway. With this paver, it is possible to achieve up to 6 ft (1.8 m) per minute.

Above: At all stages during constuction, surveys are carried out to insure that the correct dimensions and directions are being maintained.

Road finishings

Once the roadways are completed, it is possible to fill up the verges with earth and then topsoil and seed the cutting and embankment slopes. Safety barriers can be erected in the central reserve between the roadways or in the edge verges where the height of embankment may justify them. Reflectors are laid on the roadway to indicate the traffic lanes and ramp entrances, together with white lines. These white lines are composed of small spherical glass beads (called ballotini) contained in a soft plastic paint which is sprayed onto the road surface so that they are easily visible in daylight or when lit by headlights.

Street lighting and signposts are erected at the intersections and where traffic joins or leaves the new road. In towns and foggy areas, overhead lighting is often installed for safety reasons. Emergency telephone cables connected to telephones placed at intervals along the route are frequently installed in the verges. In urban areas it is possible to reduce the level of noise from traffic on the road by erecting light screens about 8 ft (2.4 m) high continuously along, and close to, the edges of the road.

See also: Concrete; Earthmoving machinery.

Road safety

In an effort to reduce the numbers of traffic accidents, over the last 30 years the field of road safety has expanded from empirical attempts with legislative moves such as urban speed limits and publicity campaigns into a comprehensive study of the whole environmental, vehicle, road user complex of modern traffic. Studies of accidents show that the environment and road users themselves are the most important factors in the occurrence of accidents. Vehicles themselves cause accidents less often, but have a great influence on the resultant injuries.

Almost every aspect of road design has an effect on accidents. In the new towns it is possible with modern layouts to design environments which are much safer than the rest of the country. For example, the segregation of pedestrians from automobiles with the provision of subways, bridges and special pedestrian and cycle routes can greatly reduce pedestrian and cycle accidents. Similarly freeways, because of restricted access and the absence of pedestrians, parked vehicles and turns across oncoming traffic, have about half the number of accidents per vehicle mile traveled than other classes of road. But many town and country highways were developed before the invention of the automobile, so road safety is mainly concerned with modifying what is already in existence.

The basic aim of all road alignments, junction designs and road signs is to simplify the decisions which have to be taken by drivers and provide enough time for those decisions to be made correctly. Thus, improving the alignments at curves with bad accident records gives up to 80 per cent reduction in the accidents occurring at those sites. At crossroads the provision of traffic circles, traffic signals, *or* the staggering of the minor roads similarly reduces accidents by about one half.

Road surface

Road surfaces influence the occurrence of accidents profoundly, and in recent years special materials have been developed for sites where heavy braking is frequent. One such surface is a calcined bauxite in a resin base; this provides high skid resistance even when wet, and does not polish significantly with use. On experimental sites, it has given a reduction of more than 30 per cent in accidents. It is, however, an expensive material, and use is generally restricted to high-risk areas, such as junctions.

The advent of high-speed divided highways poses an additional problem on the road surface in wet weather. At speeds greater than 50 mph (80 km/h), if water collects on the road, a wedge of water intrudes between the moving tire and the surface, and so reduces the effective area of contact. If the water becomes established completely beneath the tire, then all direct contact is lost and *aquaplaning* occurs. Modern tires have been developed with tread patterns designed for draining, but a more effective solution is to use a road surface which is porous, thus allowing rain to drain away into the

Left: Driving on heavily congested city highways can place a great stress on drivers, leading to much higher accident rates than on uncrowded rural roads. Accident rates can be reduced by a significant amount, however, by providing clear, easily visible signposting (as here), good lighting, and by strictly enforcing speed restrictions. The installation of lighting on a highway, for example, can reduce night-time accidents by about 30 per cent.

surface instead of having to let it run off into gutters at the sides of the road.

Lighting

About one-third of all accidents happen when it is dark, although there is more traffic during daytime. Per mile driven on freeways, for example, the nighttime accident rate is three times the daylight rate. Street lighting greatly improves the situation – if lighting is installed on a previously unlit highway a reduction of about 30 per cent in nighttime accidents can be expected.

The level of illumination is important; the more light the better, although there comes a point when additional benefits are small in comparison to the cost of higher lighting levels. Considerable technical arguments exist over the best color for street lighting, the two main types being sodium lighting which is yellow, or mercury vapor which is blue–white. There is no conclusive evidence either way and the decision is frequently made simply on esthetic grounds.

Crash barriers

Single vehicle accidents in which an automobile leaves the road and strikes a roadside object account for about one-third of all automobile occupant injuries. So the positioning and design of roadside fixtures is important, and lamp standards in particular are struck with great frequency. Attempts to reduce such incidents are often made by providing crash barriers around the lampposts or by positioning the posts themselves away from the roadside, and suspending the lights from a series of wire catenaries either across the road or along the line of the roadway. This latter solution is favored particularly in Europe. A more recent solution used in the U.S. is to have *frangible* or weak joints built into the bases of especially lightweight aluminum or steel standards. When struck by an automobile, the joint fails, allowing the car to continue, sweeping away the pole without sudden rapid deceleration.

One of the virtues of having a divided highway is the great reduction which is obtained in the frequency of severe and fatal head-on collisions. Work in the U.S. has shown that the width of the central median affects the rate of crossover accidents on highways where there is no central barrier. The standard specification for the U.S. Interstate highway system requires a median width of 50 ft (15 m). In Europe, where land acquisition is more expensive, narrow medians are preferred, usually with rigid central barriers.

A central barrier alters the types of accidents that occur, but does not necessarily reduce the overall number. At low traffic flows, an automobile may go onto the central median and then cross the opposing roadway to come to rest on the far side without having a collision. In such circumstances the presence of a median barrier would cause a collision, albeit of a glancing type with minor injury. Under those circumstances, there is a trade-off between a small number of fatal head-on accidents against a much larger number of accidents of generally lesser

Left: A truck leaving a toll plaza on the Governor Thomas E. Dewey Thruway, which connects New York City and Buffalo, the two largest cities in New York State. The Thruway has been designed with particular regard to safety: there are no intersections at ground level, no sharp curves, and no steep hills, and a sight distance of at least 1000 ft has been provided throughout to eliminate any blind spots for fast-traveling vehicles.

Above: The wide central median and the median barrier of this highway in New York State prevent vehicles from running out of control onto the opposite roadway and causing a fatal collision.

severity. At higher traffic flows, however, the presence of a median barrier on any divided highway is now considered to be imperative.

A novel solution to the automobile which runs out of control into bridge abutments and the like has become popular in the U.S. although not yet in Europe. A tolerable deceleration (on the order of 5 g) is provided by installing barriers in front of the rigid structures. They consist of plastic drums containing varying amounts of sand, and as the automobile progresses into the barrier at a reducing speed the mass of sand struck increases. This progression is so designed that a uniform, tolerable, controlled crash takes place, with only minor bruising to the occupants even from approach speeds of 60 to 70 mph (96 to 112 km/h). An alternative system is used occasionally in hilly country in Europe, at sites where vehicles are likely to run out of control because of brake failure. Arrester beds of gravel are provided at the curves where the vehicles leave the road. The gravel is of such a depth and size that the wheels sink in, and bring even a freely rolling truck to rest in a short distance.

Vehicle design

Mechanical failure of vehicles is not a significant cause of accidents, provided that maintenance is of a high standard. Many countries require older vehicles to undergo an annual inspection. Road safety can, however, be improved by appropriate vehicle design for both *primary* and *secondary* safety. Primary safety involves the factors that help to avoid accidents happening, such as good roadholding, antilock braking systems and ERGONOMIC DESIGN of the controls. Secondary safety is concerned with minimizing the effects of any accidents that do occur and includes such features as passenger restraints, laminated windshields, and deformable body structures, many of which have been introduced as a result of pressure from consumer action groups.

Road warnings

Basic ergonomics require that instructions to any machine operator (which includes a driver of any road vehicle) should be unambiguous, so timed as to be easily assimilated at the speed at which the system operates, easily observed under all the conditions which occur (including bad weather and darkness), and should fit the expectations that the driver may have. A breakdown in any one of these principles leads to error, and eventually to accident.

There is agreement between most countries in Europe and the U.S. on the standardization of road signs. This has involved the replacement of words with symbols, and agreed uniform color coding. In the U.S. some experimental installations have been made by which information is given to the driver in a nonvisual manner. This is attractive because often the eyes are overloaded in terms of the information which they have to scan and select. Warnings of approaching hazards are given through rumble strips – patches of coarse-textured road surface which produce a noise and vibration in the vehicle. Such strips are used at the approaches to junctions or bends after long straights when the driver's level of alertness may be low.

Speed limits

Speed limits have always been a controversial road safety measure. They are attractive to legislators because they cost virtually nothing, but in recent years the benefits obtained from the inappropriate use of speed restrictions have been debatable. Often there are conflicts between vehicles moving at different speeds, causing one automobile, for example, to interact with another, which gives rise to braking or overtaking, which in turn leads to errors of judgement and accidents. Hence it is desirable to have uniformity of speeds within the traffic stream; speed limits do this by reducing the number of vehicles traveling much faster than the average speed. Indeed, a technique used particularly in the U.S. for deciding on the speed limit to be applied to a particular section of highway is to measure the distribution of speeds in the traffic stream in the unrestricted condition, and then fix the speed limit at the 85th percentile level. This procedure is sound in the sense that it suits the expectations of most drivers, and in fact gives good conformity of behavior. Such a policy demands that the posted speed limit change frequently, almost with every curve and stretch of road, but it appears to be successful. Also, in the U.S., special reflecting signs have been developed which show different numbers when illuminated by headlights at night compared with daylight. By this means, the posted speed limit can be lowered automatically for the hours of darkness.

A further speed control technique is to have minimum speed limits as well as maximum ones. The effect is to reduce the number of conflicts by speeding up the slow end of the traffic stream. Accident data show that the method is particularly successful on high-speed freeways where minimum limits of 40 mph (60 km/h) are imposed.

Other aspects

Speed limits represent only one aspect of traffic management which has benefits for road safety. In urban areas the reduction of congestion, improved flows and the reduction in accidents are all complementary aims of good traffic control. Vehicle-actuated traffic signals at junctions, for example, allow changes in daily flow patterns to be accommodated and, together perhaps with all-red phases, allow conflicts at the junctions to be reduced. The

linking of traffic signals to a computer allows maximum flows and minimum delays to be obtained along an arterial road or over the whole of a city.

Pedestrian fatalities in most European countries represent almost one-third of the total number of traffic deaths. Various procedures operate to segregate in time or space the automobile from the pedestrian. Designated crossings of the zebra type, in which pedestrians have priority, are common, but pedestrian-operated light signals are being used increasingly. Underpasses and bridges are safe but expensive solutions, and studies have shown that pedestrians are willing to take risks if the safer alternative route is appreciably longer. So a necessary addition to most pedestrian bridges is the fencing needed to eliminate the other route. In the U.S., however, pedestrian segregation is more general and pedestrians tend to be better disciplined in their use of the highway – as at crossings. The result is that death rates are much lower.

As far as the environmental aspects of road safety are concerned, solutions are available to almost every problem, but the cost of the desired changes restricts their introduction. Road user behavior, however, is more difficult to control, because there is little connection established between training and codes of conduct on the one hand, and actual accident involvement on the other.

Road safety therefore is mainly an engineering problem, where the system is designed and operated in a manner which can accommodate the considerable range of human capabilities and behavior. Attempts to modify human behavior on the whole are unsuccessful and good traffic control and road-safety measures now recognize this fact.

See also: Road construction; Truck.

VOLVO PROTECTIVE CAGE

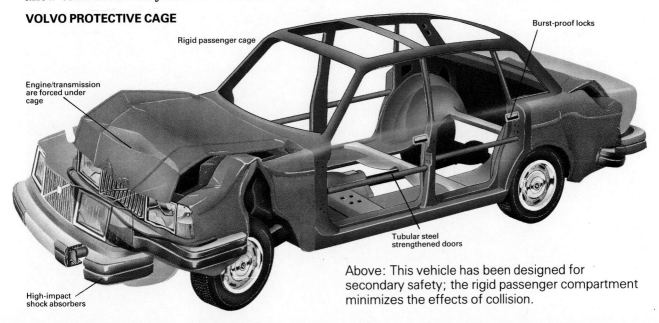

Rigid passenger cage

Burst-proof locks

Engine/transmission are forced under cage

Tubular steel strengthened doors

High-impact shock absorbers

Above: This vehicle has been designed for secondary safety; the rigid passenger compartment minimizes the effects of collision.

Robot, industrial

The term robot comes from the Czech word robota, meaning work, and was first used in a play called Rossum's Universal Robots, written in 1920 by the Czech author Karel Capek. A robot can be broadly defined as a machine that copies one or another of the functions of a human.

Industrial machines designed to handle large numbers of standard workpieces are frequently equipped with mechanical hands to move the workpieces from one station to the next. These devices can be regarded as the forerunners of the modern industrial robot, and cannot be programed or used to perform another function.

An early industrial robot, called Planabot, had a hand fixed to the end of an extendable arm. The arm could be tilted up or down to an angle of 60°, and could be rotated about a vertical axis through 360°. The wrist joint between the arm and the hand could also be rotated, and all the various movements were effected by means of hydraulic motors or jacks. The robot was programable and could be set to move between a total of up to 45 predetermined positions in a specified sequence and spend a selected time in each position.

The next stage in the evolution of the robot incorporated *information* functions, utilizing computer technology. The dexterity of robots also increased along with their information capabilities. A Unimate robot has five basic movements – arm extension and retraction, up and down movement of the arm about a vertical axis, hand rotation about the wrist axis, hand pivoting at right angles to the wrist axis, and gripping. Gripping is accomplished by a set of pneumatically operated fingers. Gripping

force can be varied up to a maximum of 359 lb (1600 newtons). The Unimate can place objects to an accuracy of about 0.04 in. (1 mm).

The arm's movements are controlled hydraulically by means of a *servo valve, servo amplifier* and *comparator*. The comparator receives sequence information – the instructions to which the robot responds – from a computer. In early second-generation robots large computers using magnetic drums were used. Now, large computers are used only in controlling large production lines; individual robots are controlled by microcomputer. Some robots have their own on-board circuitry, while others are controlled by personal computers via a suitable *interface*. Sequence information is usually stored on *floppy disks* or *hard disks*. Some robots of this type include a FEEDBACK system which monitors the effect of the instructions via an encoder so that every movement of the arm is precisely controlled.

Robot applications

The automobile industry is the greatest user of robots, but other kinds of manufacturing industry are ripe for adopting them. Other large-scale high-value manufacturing, such as the aircraft industry, is using robots, but as technology becomes cheaper other, more surprising uses will be found. Assembly lines in the electronics industry are large users of robotics, but the clothing industry is potentially a large market for industrial robots. Robots are being used by the newspaper industry for feeding presses with paper reels. These robots travel to the paper storage area, and transport the reels with no human intervention, moving without rails or any kind of external guidance system.

Japan is the largest producer and the largest market for robots. An economy with a shortage of

Right: In one of the many stages in a fully mechanized car manufacturing plant, a powerful robot swings a 44 lb (20 kg) blank metal cylinder against a furnace hammer to forge a high-pressure seal. Without robots, such an operation would require a large team of human workers controlling slow, less-efficient machinery. Moreover, the environment is noisy, hot and generally unhealthy for humans to work in.

labor had produced about 218 robotics companies by 1985. In the same year, the industrial output from robots in Japan was estimated at more than $450,000,000. Economists predict that the value of goods produced by robots in Japan could rise to three times that value by 1995.

In addition to the production line, robots can be used in places where it would be dangerous for humans to venture. The French have developed submersible robots which can operate more than 3000 ft (1000 m) beneath the sea, for example. Areas of high radiation, such as inside nuclear power plants, are ideal places to use robots, and the military are looking to use robots on the battlefield and in space.

The state of the art

Researchers are starting work on the third generation of robots, sophisticated machines with a high level of artificial intelligence. When intelligence is discussed in robotics circles, the concept means that the robots will have the ability to adapt to the environment and be capable of abstract thought.

Fully operational third-generation robots are still some way off, but at the Expo 85 exhibition in Japan an exciting departure for robotics was shown – Wabot 2. Wabot 2 is roughly humanoid in shape, instead of being another production-line oriented device. It plays an electronic organ with its hands and feet – its limbs have 25 axes of movement. Wabot 2 reads a sheet of music in 15 seconds, using a *charge-coupled device* camera.

Below: A robot applying glue to components of a car body prior to assembly.
Below right: Polishing sink units. This robot is programed to move through 200 set positions.

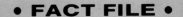

• FACT FILE •

- Light-sensitive welding robots have helped Japan achieve supremacy in the building of giant oil tankers. The steel plates of the tankers' structure are treated with coatings and markings that reflect varying degrees of light, attracting the robots' positioning mechanisms to the exact welding site.

- Agricultural robots in use in the U.S. pick and sort citrus fruit at a rate of 20 tons per day. Sensors built into the robot enable it to sort the crop into six size categories and four color grades.

- The earliest of all robots may have been mechanisms powered by steam that were employed by priests in ancient Egypt to open up the massive temple doors, instilling awe and reverence in the watching congregation.

- The Programable Robot Observer With Logical Enemy Response (PROWLER) looks like a tank, acts like a sentry, and has been designed to patrol perimeter fences. The equipment can be custom-built for specific applications – one prototype was fitted with twin M60 machine guns and a grenade launcher.

See also: Assembly line; Computer.

A robot does it better

Toshio Iguchi, a small Japanese industrialist, works about three hours a day. If he is too busy to go to work, his wife pops into the factory to check up on the workers. Toshio's company, Iguchi Seisakusho, manufactures plastic parts for toys. As well as being president of the company, he is the only employee – three robots do all the work.

Meanwhile, at a car assembly plant in Birmingham, England, the production line foreman takes the trainee welder through his new job. Guiding his hand, like a parent teaching his child to write, the foreman shows the new boy exactly what he must do. When it is the welder's turn, he does it all exactly right. And goes on doing it – time after time.

Robots are a fact of industrial life. They are tireless workers who never go on strike or mind unduly if the factory has more in common with hell than with a late twentieth century industrialized nation.

The simplest robot is a basic unit which can be programed to carry out a short task repeatedly – like Toshio Iguchi's robots, which feed raw materials to injection molding machines and cut sets of finished components apart. At the other end of the scale are the monsters used on car assembly tracks which make up to 300 welds on a body shell within mi-nutes, their long arms reaching into and under the car, the entire assembly moving some 30 ft (9 m) during the operation. Somewhere in between lie the high-speed robots which can see what they are doing, sorting out parts of a different shape or color, and handling incredibly delicate objects like integrated circuits and light-bulb filaments.

Robots are not cheap. Added to the purchase price of the unit must be installation charges, the cost of the ancillary equipment, and the cost of disrupting a factory while the robot is installed. Today's high capital costs can be blamed on the comparatively complex design of most machines and the functions they must perform. Possibly the simplest part of any robot is its *arm,* a manipulator which usually imitates the human arm, wrist and hand very closely. The *hand* or *end effector* can be anything from a mechanical gripper on a vacuum cup to tools such as welding torches, sprayguns and specialized units for a single purpose.

The heart of any robot (the part that makes it more than just another machine) is its *brain.* The more expensive the brain, the more versatile the robot. As technology becomes cheaper – or, rather, as cheap technology gets more advanced – we are starting to enter a new generation of robotics. First generation robots still account for about 80 per cent of the world's current robot population. They are simple machines which have been programed by their manufacturers to carry out a number of easy

Left: A Fata welding station equipped with a turntable and robots specially adapted for electric welding. The robots are programed as they are taken through the task by a human welder, in much the same way that a teacher guides a child's hand to write its first letters. The actions are recorded and replayed to control the robot subsequently.

Above: An automatic wheel assembly robot picks up and fits front and rear wheels, complete with tires, to cars on a conveyer.

Above: A robot-controlled autofeed drill making holes in an airplane wing spar. The control head can be preset to maintain feed rate and depth.

tasks. The manipulator moves in a straight line from point to point, and is really suitable only for boring repetitive tasks like transferring materials from one part of a production line to another. But they are cheap: even if they do not increase the production rate they can reduce labor costs and release employees for other, more satisfying work.

The second generation of robots is much more glamorous. They are called playback robots and come in two types. Their brains are capable of learning a task by heart – the operator simply has to lead the arm through the motions and operations necessary for the job. Afterward the robot does it by itself.

It is here that the difference between the two types becomes apparent. The first type is the continuous path (CP) robot. Programing it is simple: the operator leads it through the operation. The robot's brain repeats and remembers each part of the movement, storing the movement as a huge number of small steps. To reprogram the robot the operator leads its through a new set of movements.

By contrast, point to point robots (PTPs), although taught in the same way, translate the operation into a series of points through which the manipulator must pass. To reprogram the robot, the operator alters the coordinates of the manipulator's reference points held in the *brain*.

What of the future? The new generation of robots is with us now. It has eyes, a nose and very sensitive fingertips that can feel texture, hardness and weight. One well-publicized example is the

sniffer robot used by British Leyland Cars at their new plant in Cowley, England. To check for leaks around the windshield and doors the car is filled with helium. The robot's two *sniffer heads* then move over every seam, seal and aperture in the body checking for the slightest leak.

Another motor company, FIAT in Italy, has been using robots for several years. Their latest development in this field is a robot with eyes. At the moment it is used only to bolt hinges to doors, but the principle has been tested and applied – under experimental conditions – to other production processes. The robot uses a TV camera interfaced with a computer and preprocessor. The camera scans the edge of the door while the system analyzes a carefully lit part of the area round one of the sets of bolt holes. The camera picture is split into 250,000 separate picture elements which are separated by the preprocessor into black and white. The resulting checkerboard pattern (resembling a grainy black-and-white photograph of the object) is then passed to the computer which compares it with an ideal one held in its memory. The computer pinpoints the centers of the two bolt holes and directs the arm holding the hinge and bolts toward them.

The relentless march of robotics cannot be stopped. Robots will sooner or later invade every part of our lives. Together with the microchip, they represent a revolution as far-reaching as the industrial revolution of the eighteenth century. The Luddites who opposed it were proven wrong.

Rocket

The term rocket loosely applies both to any nonair-breathing engine and to the vehicle it propels. Small rockets, which carry scientific instruments on short *parabolic* flights to the edge of the atmosphere, are called *sounding rockets*. Large multi-stage devices designed to carry spacecraft into orbit are more correctly called *launch vehicles,* and their propulsion units are usually described as *rocket engines* (if liquid-fueled) or *rocket motors* (if solid-fueled). The terms are flexibly applied and, particularly in the U.S., engine tends to mean larger propulsion units of both types, whereas motor refers to smaller ones.

Basic principle
Newton's Third Law of motion – to every action there is an equal and opposite reaction – is the basic principle of rocket propulsion. Turn up the water in a garden hose and watch the nozzle jump back. Cover half the nozzle with your thumb and feel the extra strain on the nozzle as the water suddenly

streams farther and faster. Likewise, eject anything from the rear of a rocket and the rocket will move forward. The velocity of the rocket will increase if mass is ejected at high speed. So the escape of burning expanding gases, accelerated by passing through a constricted nozzle, propels a rocket engine in the opposite direction.

History
The first known form of rocket appeared in the early thirteenth century in China, following close on the invention of gunpowder, and was simply an arrow with a tube of powder lashed to it. The improvement into *stick-stabilized* rockets was rapid, as was the spread westward, so that, by the mid-thirteenth century, first the Mongols and then the Arabs were using rockets in battle. The French crusaders brought them to Europe, and French troops under Joan of Arc defended Orleans with rockets in 1429. By this time, however, cannon and small arms were proving more accurate and effective, so that the rocket faded from the military scene, if not the festive one, for the next 350 years.

Then, in 1792, British troops fighting in India were heavily assailed by small metal-cased rockets with an effectiveness that revived British respect for the military potential of such devices. It was the director of Woolwich Arsenal, Colonel (later Sir William) Congreve, who, by 1804, developed this device into an efficient and destructive naval weapon with an incendiary or explosive warhead.

The accuracy, however, remained far from satisfactory until the mid-nineteenth century when the

Left: A V2 rocket being launched in Germany. V2s were used by Hitler during World War II.
Below: A ground-to-ground rocket fired from a self-propelled amphibious launching pad.

Above: Testing a long-range MX missile for its tolerance to the vibrations of its own engine. One method of deploying MX missiles is to mount them in a network of silos in an open desert. The missiles would be moved between the silos in an attempt to render enemy information inaccurate.

Below: The Pershing II intermediate-range nuclear missile has a two-staged launch vehicle. It can be deployed as a Multiple Independently targeted Re-entry Vehicle (MIRV) that can attack several targets from a single launch.

Englishman William Hale applied *spin-stabilization* by means of curved vanes in the exhaust nozzle. Range was still limited in relation to size until 1855 when an idea for stacking two rockets together was first applied by Colonel Boxer. The result was a two-stage, line-carrying, life-saving rocket in which the exhausted first stage ignited the second stage via an explosive separation charge.

Meanwhile, the propellant potential of combustible liquids and the broader applications of rocket power were becoming increasingly appreciated and numerous people are credited with devising rocket machinery of amazing foresight or absurdity. The first realistic theoretician was Russia's Konstantin E. Tsiolkovsky who, as early as 1883, recognized the potential of the rocket in space. He first understood the significance of increasing exhaust velocity, the importance of mass ratio (launch weight to engine burn-out weight) and their relationship in increasing vehicle velocity. This led him into extensive study of multistaging techniques, in parallel and in tandem arrangements, efforts that subsequently earned him the title of the father of spaceflight.

His work also inspired the pioneers of modern rocketry, notably in the Soviet Union, Germany and the U.S. In the Soviet Union, rocketry was given official status from the start in 1929, when research began at the Gas Dynamics Laboratory in Leningrad (GDL). In 1933, GDL linked up with Moscow's enthusiastic Group for Jet Propulsion Research (GJRD) and, with military financing, built liquid-fueled rockets which flew to a record 3.5 miles (5.6 km) altitude in 1936.

Germany's pioneer was Hermann Oberth, a theoretician whose concepts in liquid-fuel rocketry prompted a group of young engineers to form the

VFR (Society for Space Travel) in 1927. The VFR's practical experiments laid the foundation for Germany's wartime lead in rocketry. After it dispersed in 1934 under Nazi opposition, military research absorbed some of its members, notably Wernher von Braun, later to lead development of the V-2 rocket and then to become the guiding light of the U.S.'s work up to the Apollo program. In the U.S., however, the pioneer was physicist Robert Goddard whose own small group struggled on limited private financing from the early 1920s, launching the world's first liquid-fueled rocket in 1926 and continuing with distinctive success until Goddard's death in 1945.

By 1945 the U.S., if still uninterested in spaceflight, had become aware of the new vogue of war rockets – the ballistic missile. It was the fall of Germany and the seizure of its world-beating rocket technology by both the Soviet Union and the U.S. that lent the final impetus to full-scale rocket development, unchecked until astronauts stepped onto the Moon.

Rocket systems

Increasingly diverse methods have been used for generating rocket exhaust, but the basic Newtonian law often remains the only common factor. The comparative criterion, however, of any propellant (or propulsion system) is its *specific impulse* (I_{sp}). The *thrust* is simply the force the rocket exhaust can exert on a surface – the launch pad, for example. I_{sp} indicates the number of pounds of thrust available per second from every pound of propellant consumed. It is measured in seconds and is directly related to the speed of the exhaust. An I_{sp} of about 102 seconds provides an exhaust velocity of 0.62 miles/s (1 km/s). The higher the I_{sp}, the lower the fuel mass needed for any specific thrust level.

High-thrust rockets

High-thrust systems, in which I_{sp} thrust greatly exceeds the engine weight, are necessary where gravity must be opposed, as in planetary lift-off and soft landing. The main contenders are chemical and nuclear rockets. Chemical types take two forms: solid fuel and liquid fuel. Both produce exhaust through combustion and must therefore carry their own oxygen supply. Solids are basically powder-packed squibs, the *charge* being a mix of dry fuel and a dry, oxygen-rich chemical (such as a mix of polyisobutene and ammonium perchlorate). They offer simplicity and reliability, but a lower I_{sp} and, being all combustion chamber, a heavy structure.

Below: The Apollo 16 spacecraft lifts off from then-named Cape Kennedy to make a lunar landing in 1972.

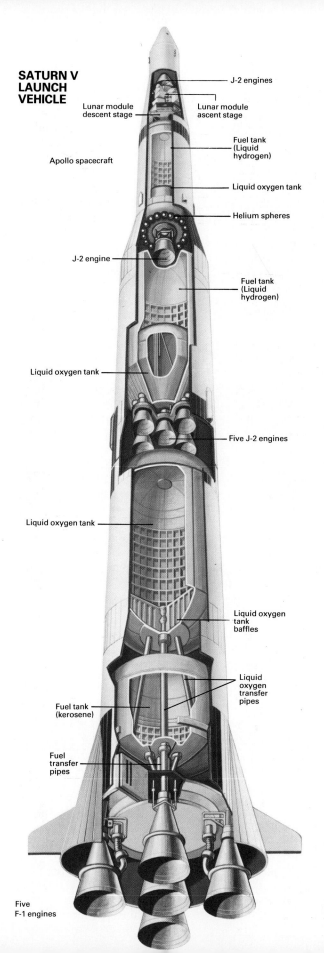

SATURN V LAUNCH VEHICLE

J-2 engines

Lunar module descent stage

Lunar module ascent stage

Apollo spacecraft

Fuel tank (Liquid hydrogen)

Liquid oxygen tank

Helium spheres

J-2 engine

Fuel tank (Liquid hydrogen)

Liquid oxygen tank

Five J-2 engines

Liquid oxygen tank

Liquid oxygen tank baffles

Liquid oxygen transfer pipes

Fuel tank (kerosene)

Fuel transfer pipes

Five F-1 engines

Left: The Saturn V rocket used by Apollo Moon Missions was powered by five kerosene/liquid oxygen engines in the first stage and by liquid oxygen/liquid hydrogen engines in subsequent stages.

They cannot be controlled except in burn rate.

Modern liquid-fuel engines, in which fuel, such as hydrazine or liquid hydrogen, and an oxidizer, such as liquid oxygen, are pumped separately into a small combustion chamber, can be stopped, restarted and throttled at will. But the price is complexity and reduced reliability.

Some form of nuclear propulsion is seen as the high-thrust system of the future. Solid-core devices which release heat from a fission reaction have already been ground-tested in the Soviet Union and the U.S. Fuel pumped through perforations in the reactor core is superheated and expelled through a nozzle. The FUSION rocket, which at the moment is purely speculative, would exploit a hydrogen conversion process similar to that in the Sun itself – and with comparably high energy output. FISSION of 1 lb of uranium, or fusion of 1 lb of heavy hydrogen, produces two million times the energy obtained from burning 1 lb of kerosene.

But greater attention is being given to the idea of streaming nuclear bomblets behind a thrust shield where they are positioned by a magnetic field and detonated by laser beam. This could provide the hard acceleration for quick orbital escape or entry, or fast interplanetary flight. In the early 1950s, Project Orion in the U.S. looked at the possibility of using a rocket driven by nuclear explosions as a launch vehicle, but the project was abandoned, making way for the less efficient chemical rocket, when it became clear that such a vehicle would contaminate large stretches of the Earth's atmosphere with radioactive material. Such a propulsion, though, might be tolerable in space.

Scaled-down chemical rockets are used to power orbit change, interplanetary course corrections and, in miniature form, for attitude control of probes and satellites and for rocket-stage and payload separation. Solids are used if only one burn is needed (as in *stage separation*). Spacecraft control thrusters tend to have *monopropellants* (fuel and oxidizer in a single fluid) or *hypergolic* chemicals which ignite on mutual contact. Tank pressurization forces the propellants into the chamber under the control of simple valves; I_{sp} is low but reliability is greater.

Low-thrust rockets

Unfortunately, under current technology, high I_{sp} systems offer only a minute thrust in relation to engine weight, so they are practical only where INERTIA is the sole opposition. The most promising of these is the electrostatic or ion rocket, already test-flown in space, which works by isolating mercury or cesium

Left: A Soviet A2 rocket lifts off carrying another Soyuz mission into orbit. The Soyuz spacecraft are used to ferry cosmonauts to and from the Salyut Space Station. Similar rockets are used to launch unpiloted Progress supply ships. Right: Ariane's three-stage 236-ton rocket was successfully launched from Kourou, French Guiana, on December 24, 1979. The rocket was expected to maintain a geostationary orbit, in which the satellite circles the planet in the same time it takes the Earth to spin on its axis (24 hours) and appears stationary from Earth.

ions and accelerating them to produce exhaust. The thrust is tiny (about 1/100 oz, 0.2835 g), but with its compact fuel load and nuclear generator, an ion-powered spacecraft could keep accelerating gently for months and years, eventually developing phenomenal speeds. Deep-space missions are the main application but, within ten years, Earth satellites will also be carrying ion engines for orbital positioning and attitude control.

In the still theoretical electromagnetic or *plasma* rocket, a fuel such as hydrogen is converted to an electrically ionized gas by an electric arc, then accelerated out by a magnetic field. Nuclear fission is also under study for this category in the form of a gaseous core rocket where fuel is passed through a gaseous reactor, suspended in the chamber by magnetic fields. This concept, like others using magnetic fields for containment and position, faces the major technological hurdle of achieving accuracy in magnet-field control.

Of all the exotic ideas under discussion, including photon drive, which uses a beam of light particles for thrust, the space ramjet and laser radiation, only hydrogen fusion shows promise of succeeding. Using a nuclear pulse motor, a rapid succession of deuterium-originated nuclear explosions would be a spacecraft's power source. Such an engine, when constructed, is calculated to have an exhaust velocity of 6000 miles/s (10,000 km/s), which is several hundred times that of the most advanced ion-drive engine under test and certainly powerful enough for interstellar travel.

Typical I_{sp} values

Typical I_{sp} values are as follows: Chemical rockets: solid, 245 seconds (s); liquid oxygen (lox)-kerosene (Saturn 5 first stage), 260 s (sea level); lox-liquid hydrogen (LH_2 – Saturn 5 upper stages), 456 s (vacuum). Nuclear rockets: solid core-LH_2, 600 to 1500 s; gaseous core, 3000 s; and bomblets, 1000 s. The value for ion is 10,000 to 100,000 s; plasma, up to 20,000 s; photon, up to 10 million.

Construction and launch

Rocket research is largely focused on the chemical engine – finding better propellants and more efficient ways of exploiting them. The main challenge is in the materials required to cope with ever-increasing extremes of operating temperature and pressure or to produce the right flexibility, rigidity, lightness, purity or thermal conductivity. Copper alloys tend to be used for lining combustion chambers whereas aluminum alloys are used normally for structural elements.

In the U.S., engines are usually designed specifically for a particular booster stage, each stage being a self-contained rocket. Specialist firms are paid by NASA to produce competitive preliminary designs so that the best can be selected. Usually, one of the major aircraft companies builds the structures, tanks and controls and installs the engines, different stages of a booster often being built in different parts of the country. The stages are brought separately to the launch site by air, road or (for the giant Saturn 5 lower stages) by barge, and assembled vertically on the launch pad. The Saturn 1B and 5 Apollo launchers, however, are *stacked* in Cape Canaveral's Vertical Assembly Building, the world's largest building, and then carried erect by the huge crawler transporter to the launch pad 1.5 miles (2.4 km) away. The Soviet Union's main booster, designated the Standard S vehicle, is of more robust construction than U.S. boosters and is assembled horizontally, carried to the launch pad by rail car and erected piecemeal.

Countdown can begin days before launch to schedule in complex fueling, checkout and contingency operations. Final ignition sequence is usually automatic from about zero minus three minutes. Ignition is achieved either electrically, explosively or from hypergolic chemicals. Restraining arms hold the rocket for 2 to 4 seconds or until full thrust has built up. As the rocket ascends, the thinning air allows the exhaust flame to broaden and shorten. Upper stage engines designed to operate purely in space tend to have longer, narrower engine bells to contain the exhaust flow. Directional control is often achieved, especially on solids, by swiveling the bell. During ascent, power is sometimes reduced to ease acceleration loads, either by early cut-out of one engine in a cluster or from burn-out of small, strap-on, half-stage rockets. First stage burn-out and jettison usually occurs at 30 to 50 miles (48 to 80 km) altitude and one or more upper stages takes the payload onto the orbital height of 200 miles (322 km) or more and a speed of 17,500 mph (28,160 km/h). Orbit is achieved 12 to 13 minutes after lift-off.

See also: Space photography; Space shuttle; Space suit; Space telescope; Space vehicle.

Rolling, metal

Rolling is a process used to convert cast metals into semifinished and finished products. About 90 per cent of steel production, for example, is rolled. In principle the process is simple: a pair of cylindrical rollers made of iron or steel rotate in opposite directions with a gap between them which is smaller than the cross section of the piece which is to be rolled. The workpiece is entered into the gap and as it passes between the rolls it is squeezed, its cross section being progressively reduced. Because the working volume remains constant, the result of one pass through the rolls is a lengthening of the workpiece and a precise reduction and shaping of the cross section.

Despite its basic simplicity, the modern rolling mill with all its control equipment for manipulating the stock is an immensely complex piece of engineering. The forces involved are enormous. As the workpiece passes through the roll gap, it exerts forces on the rolls, causing them to bend and spring apart: in a large mill, these forces could easily attain several hundred tons. The rolls must therefore be mounted in massive steel housings capable of minimizing the deflections that occur. Excessive de-flections would spoil the shape and dimensions of the emergent workpiece.

A set of rolls mounted in a pair of housings is called a *stand*. Single-stand mills are common but quite often two or more stands are used together to make a *mill train*. Several arrangements are possible: for example, a *looping train* has several stands placed side by side with adjacent stands necessarily operating in different directions, whereas a *tandem train* has two or more stands following each other in a straight line. Often, all the stands in a train operate simultaneously on the same workpiece. Powerful electric motors are used to drive the rolls and, in *reversing* mills, must be capable of periodic reversal to change the direction of rotation of the rolls as the work is fed back through them.

Rolling may be carried out either hot or cold. Hot rolling is the most common process, especially for the initial working of cast ingots for which the lower rolling forces required give lower costs. Hot rolling is a combination of working and annealing and is an effective method of breaking up the *as-cast* structure of the ingot, and can also close up certain cast-

Below: The manufacture of a steel girder in a metal-forging plant. A range of complex shaped sections can be made, including seamless tubing.

in internal flaws. During hot rolling, the metal structure deformed by the working recrystallizes and softens, or anneals, to remove the hardening effect of the working. For this process to take place, the hot rolling temperature has to be greater than the recrystallization temperature of the metal being worked. An increase of about 150° F (65° C) gives a *finishing temperature* that insures a fine, uniform grain structure. A typical rolling temperature for carbon steel is 2200° F (1200° C). The finish produced by hot rolling is generally slightly rough, because it has a coating of *mill scale*.

Cold rolling is carried out at room temperatures (though with some metals, such as lead, this temperature is high enough for hot working) and has the effect of hardening the metal. This strain hardening can increase the strength of the finished product, but where further working is required the metal has to be annealed to restore it to a soft condition. Cold working can produce a much better surface finish then hot working, together with more accurate finished dimensions.

Flat rolling
Rolling mills for processing metal ingots are known as *blooming* or *slabbing* mills. Generally, blooms are square in cross section, with a thickness of 6 in. (150 mm) or more, but slabs have a rectangular shape. Blooms are further rolled to give billets

Below: Forging an alloy wall casing on an open-die forging press. The alloy is shaped on a high-temperature steel former which rotates inside the hot metal cylinder. The finished casing is used to reinforce high-stress structures.

SHEET METAL PRODUCTION

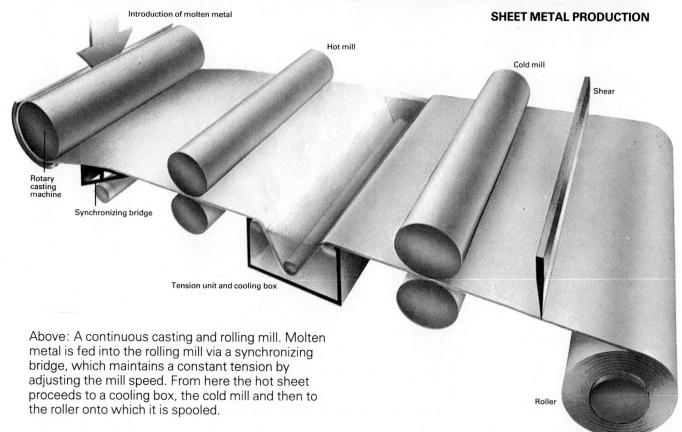

Above: A continuous casting and rolling mill. Molten metal is fed into the rolling mill via a synchronizing bridge, which maintains a constant tension by adjusting the mill speed. From here the hot sheet proceeds to a cooling box, the cold mill and then to the roller onto which it is spooled.

which are then processed into sections, such as rails, angles, and channels.

For rolling plates, sheets and strip, each roll approximates to a plain cylinder (the diameter is often increased slightly at the center to compensate for roll bending) and different reductions are accomplished by varying the separation of the rolls. Products vary from plates as thick as about 12 in. (300 mm), for use in heavy engineering, to strip only a few microns thick (1 micron is 0.0000394 in.) for the electronics industry. In terms of productivity, the most highly developed example of flat rolling is the continuous production, in multistand tandem mills, of the steel base for tinplate.

The metal may emerge from the final stand at speeds exceeding 60 mph (96 km/h), so the engineering of ancillary equipment, such as coilers and flying shears, represents a considerable achievement. The rolling forces can be reduced by the use of smaller diameter rolls because this reduces the contact arc between the metal and the roll.

Section rolling
For this type of product, grooves of the appropriate profile must be cut into the rolls. Each pair of rolls is provided with a number of grooves of decreasing area and progressively varying shape, according to the complexity of the required product. The distance between the rolls is normally kept constant, the necessary reduction being accomplished by passing the workpiece successively through progressively smaller grooves, the direction of movement being reversed for each pass.

Tubular products
Seamless tubes are manufactured by opening out the center of an ingot or billet in a piercing mill and then working the resulting shell to produce the correct diameter and wall thickness. Rotary piercing may be carried out in a Mannesmann mill, which consists of a pair of rolls with their axes angled to each other and rotating in the same direction. The action of the rolls rotates and deforms the workpiece as it is passed between them and causes a crack to open along the central axis. As the crack opens, the workpiece is forced onto a pointed plug that opens up the crack and shapes the hole with the resulting tube being fed onto a mandrel that carries the plug.

See also: Aluminum; Metal; Steel manufacture.

Left: After recovery from the ore, metals are supplied in bulk or processed to form alloys, also in bulk form. The bulk metals are further processed into useable forms, such as sheet metal, as here. Aluminum is shaped at room temperature by the cold-rolling metal process, during which the aluminum hardens into foil of accurate dimensions and a high-quality finish. The foil has a high polish to prevent abrasion during rolling and unrolling of the rolls.

Rope manufacture

Rope may be described as a cord at least 0.16 in. (4 mm) in diameter made by *closing* (twisting together) three or more strands which are themselves formed of twisted yarns.

Rope was one of the earliest inventions, and in many respects it has changed very little over the centuries. Materials, however, have varied and today some 90 per cent of ropes are made from synthetic FIBERS. The oldest cordage discovered (about 1000 BC) was of flax fiber, although cave paintings of 1800 BC show a twisted rope structure being used for climbing. Many vegetable fibers have been used in ropemaking, including date palm, flax, jute, cotton and *coir* (coconut fiber). Toward the end of the nineteenth century, *Manila hemp* was introduced and this soon became the most popular fiber and led to improved processing machinery.

Another hard fiber, *sisal,* was introduced in the early 1900s and, although not as popular as Manila hemp, was a very useful alternative during and after the two World Wars. Sisal has been used extensively to make baling twine for hay and straw, although increasing quantities of synthetic twine are now being sold for this job. In the 1950s, nylon and the polyester fabric Dacron were found to be excellent synthetic fibers for ropemaking, and these are the strongest materials available for normal commercial purposes.

Modern ropemaking processes

Natural fiber rope and certain synthetic ropes are made from yarn which has been spun from raw fibers. The material is fed into a *goods* or *hackling* machine which combs the fibers with steel pins and produces a coarse *sliver*. The process is repeated on other similar machines, the spacing between the pins being reduced each time so that the sliver is brought into a more regular form. The sliver is then condensed in drawing machines before being spun and wound onto bobbins. The resulting yarn can have a right-handed (Z) or left-handed (S) twist.

Synthetic yarns, such as nylon and polyester, are extruded by the manufacturers in the form of continuous filaments, and these have to be built up to a suitably sized composite yarn by plying together a number of the filaments. This is known as *doubl-*

Below: The register plate of a large rope-making machine. Ropes were once made of natural fibers.

Below: The manufacture of cable. Raw fibers are compressed into a sliver which is twisted into yarn, which in turn is twisted in the opposite direction into rope. Finally, the rope is formed into cable, the direction of twist again being reversed.

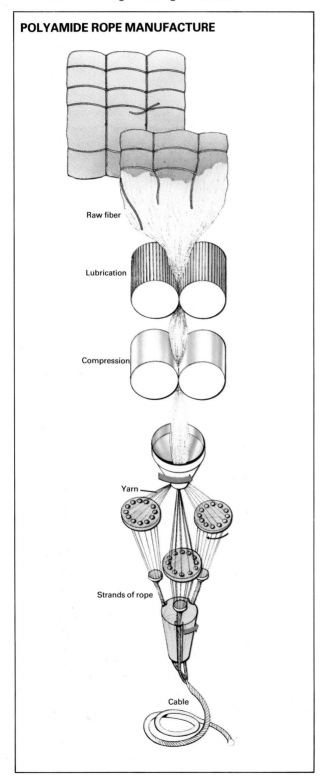

POLYAMIDE ROPE MANUFACTURE

Raw fiber

Lubrication

Compression

Yarn

Strands of rope

Cable

ing or *throwing*. The yarns are then set onto a *creel* (a frame holding bobbins of yarn) for forming the strand of a rope. For a conventional three-stranded, right-hand rope, Z yarns would be used. The ends are fed through a *register plate* which insures the correct formation of the strand, keeping the inside yarns located in the center, thus obtaining optimum strength and reducing strand failure. The yarns then enter a *compression tube* which locates the point of twisting and helps to form a smooth strand having a compact cross section. The formed strand is drawn through the tube and S twist is applied, the opposite direction to the yarn twist. On house machines the strand is hauled by capstans and wound onto strand bobbins. Once these bobbins are filled with strand they are transferred to the *closing machine.* They are mounted individually at one end of the closer and the strands are brought together at the other end, a *laying top* being used to fix the point of twist. The rope is then passed through a die. Now Z twist is applied and the rope is *closed*, the finished rope being drawn through again by means of capstans or haul pulleys and wound onto a reel. To assist the closing process, the individual strands receive extra twisting to compensate for the loss of turn by the laying into rope.

Another method of making rope is by means of a *ropewalk,* which is a path along which rope-forming strands are laid. The strands are drawn out by a *traveler* and, when they have been drawn to the correct length, the rope is closed by means of a *top-cart,* which is returned from the traveler end to the register plate end at a regulated speed.

Structure of rope
The amount of twist in a rope is called the *lay,* a *hard laid* rope having more twist put into the strand and rope than a *soft laid* rope. A three-stranded rope is known as *plain* or *hawser laid,* and a four-stranded rope, useful for rope ladders, is known as *shroud laid. Cable laid* ropes are constructed from three or more stranded ropes, and the twist direction is again reversed, in other words Z twist ropes would be cable laid with S twist.

In recent years, large braided ropes have been developed for mooring ships, and these reduce wastage by eliminating kinking. The most widely used of these ropes, called *cross plait,* is one in which eight strands are formed: four S direction using Z yarn and four Z direction using S yarn. These are produced on normal stranding machines, and a special closing machine then plaits the rope in pairs of strands – two Z strands followed by two S strands and so on. This construction produces a very flexible rope and is particularly suitable for nylon and polyester ropes where wastage is expensive.

See also: Fiber, natural; Fiber, synthetic.

Rubber, natural

Natural rubber is a material derived from the Hevea tree, a native of Brazil, and from certain other trees and shrubs. The rubber is present as *latex* which is a milk-like fluid found in a distinct area between the bark and the trunk of the tree with its normal sap system. When the bark is cut or damaged, the latex seeps out; as it dries the rubber in it forms a protective film over the damaged part.

The natives of the Amazon region called the tree *Cahuchu* or *Cauchu*, meaning "the tree that weeps." This name is still preserved in *caoutchouc* and *Kautschuck*, the French and German names for rubber. The English name is descriptive of the first use which was found for the material, in the mid-eighteenth century, for rubbing pencil marks from paper. A primitive industry in Brazil produced rubber footwear by coagulating latex, layer upon layer, onto clay formers smoked over a fire. Waterproof tents and cloaks were made by drying out latex, sandwiched between two sheets of cloth.

The first industrial use of rubber copied the primitive techniques. The rubber came mainly from the state of Para, where it was collected in the form of roughly spherical masses, about the size of a man's head, produced by dipping a wooden pole or paddle into the latex and then holding it over the smoke from a fire. In this way the rubber was built up in a series of thin layers, until it reached the required size, when it was cut free from the wooden support. The solid rubber was dissolved in coal tar naphtha, and the solution used for making dipped goods, such as galoshes and gloves, and for impregnating fabrics to make them waterproof. These garments, called *Mackintoshes* after their inventor, were certainly waterproof, but they were sensitive to heat, being hard and brittle on cold days and sticky and smelly when the weather was hot.

Goodyear in the U.S. and Hancock in England, in 1839–40, found out how to stabilize rubber, by

Below: Tapping a rubber tree in Malaysia. The tapper cuts away strips of bark in a diagonal pattern to a depth of less than one-tenth of an inch, releasing the latex which flows into the cup.

Below: Two or three hours after being tapped, the flow of latex ceases, and the container of latex is ready to be collected for processing at a central plant serving the whole plantation.

combining sulfur with it. Depending on the percentage of sulfur added, a range of products could be made, from soft extensible rubber bands or sheeting to hard inextensible *ebonite* or *vulcanite*. This *vulcanized* rubber was stable over a wide range of temperature and could be molded into commercial articles with well-defined permanent shapes in the process of vulcanization by heat.

In 1876, the British Government sent Sir Henry Wickham to Brazil, to collect rubber seeds for shipment to Malaya and Ceylon. After wintering in the orchid houses at Kew, London, the plants were taken out to form the basis of the organized rubber plantations of today.

On plantations today, latex is collected by cutting inclined grooves into the bark of the Hevea tree and allowing the latex to collect in a cup attached to the tree near its base. After collection, the latex is purified by filtration and passed to tanks where it is diluted with water. Coagulation is then induced by adding a chemical such as formic or acetic acid (this must be done within 24 hours of collection of the latex). The rubber comes out of suspension as crumbs which are dried and pressed into sheet form in a mill. Some part of the output is smoked in wood-fired drying rooms while the remainder forms the yellow *crepe* as used in shoe soles.

Chemical composition

Rubber is an unsaturated HYDROCARBON, of basic formula $(C_5H_8)_n$, where n is about 3000. The basic unit in the molecule is isoprene, $CH_2=CH-C(CH_3)=CH_2$, which occurs in turpentine. The composition of rubber was proved in 1860, when rubber was broken down into isoprene on heating, and confirmed in 1884 when Tilden produced rubber by the accidental POLYMERIZATION of isoprene which had been left standing in a bottle.

The outstanding property of rubber is its capacity to stretch to four or five times its original length, and then to recover, unchanged, when released. This may be traced to the form of the molecule which has as its backbone a long chain of carbon

Left: Dried latex crumb being compressed into bales. The traditional method of processing latex is to coagulate it by adding a chemical, such as formic or acetic acid; the latex emerges from this process in crumb form. The crumb is then dried, and either pressed into sheets or compressed into bales, as shown here.
Above: Newly coagulated latex being pressed into sheets in a Malaysian rubber processing plant.

• FACT FILE •

- During World War II, when the Japanese army had overrun the Far Eastern rubber-producing regions, both the U.S.S.R. and the U.S. experimented with plantations of dandelions, which contain small amounts of natural rubber.

- In the eighteenth century a French explorer sent specimens of rubber to France from South America, and described waterproof shoes made by local natives from single pieces of rubber. He also described how they made flasks using liquid rubber and molds.

- Although most natural rubber is made from the collected latex of the Hevea tree, in northern Mexico rubber is derived from the high-altitude guayule shrub. The whole shrub, which contains 20 per cent rubber, is shredded and mixed with water so that the rubber floats to the surface.

Below: Latex is concentrated and partly dehydrated by being spun in a centrifuge — the rotor housing of which appears in the foreground. Latex for foam rubber is usually centrifuged.

atoms. A carbon atom which is bonded by four single BONDS behaves as if it were at the center of a tetrahedron, or four-faced pyramid. Successive bonds between carbon atoms can be considered as being formed by joining the pyramids point to point. This means that, as a long chain is formed, it turns at random, depending on the point of each tetrahedron at which the bond is made. In this way a model can be made of the molecule, by bending a wire at the appropriate angle, in a random fashion. The wire coils back on itself, like a spring, and this gives an idea of the way a rubber molecule can be distorted under stress and then recover its original shape.

Uses

The bulk of the world's production of natural rubber soon came from the plantations, which spread beyond Malaya and Ceylon notably into the Dutch East Indies. Today the world production is approximately 3½ million tons per annum. Over 90 per cent of this is in the form of dry rubber and the rest is concentrated latex, for the production of rubber foam and dipped goods.

The largest use of rubber came with the development of road transportation. First came tires, in solid form, for carriages and bicycles. After Dunlop's reinvention in 1890 of the pneumatic tire, the air tire developed rapidly, first for bicycles, and later for automobiles, trucks, aircraft, tractors and earth-moving machines.

It was found, in the 1920s, that the resistance of a tire tread to wear could be increased many times by adding *carbon black* to the rubber–sulfur mix in the plastic state before vulcanization. This material, which has a very fine particle size, is formed when natural gas or oil is burned under controlled conditions with a restricted amount of air. Other materials are milled into the rubber, on steel roller mills, at this stage. They may include resins, tars, clay, colorings and organic rubber chemicals to speed up vulcanization, retard aging or modify physical properties.

Outside the tire industry, rubber is used in many products. Some of these, such as waterproof clothing and footwear, gloves and surgical goods, go back to the earlier recognized property – resistance to water. Good air retention leads to the use of rubber in air beds, inflatable boats and life rafts. Its electric resistance makes it valuable as a sheathing for the insulation of cables.

Many of these uses of natural rubber have been taken over by the synthetic product, but natural rubber nevertheless remains more satisfactory for the manufacture of the largest truck and earth-mover tires, where it provides the coolest-running compounds.

See also: Rubber, synthetic; Tire manufacture.

Rubber, synthetic

The first need to produce synthetic rubber on a manufacturing scale came during World War I, when Germany was cut off from supplies from the outside world. The technique was clear, since it was known that the large rubber molecule could be built up by the POLYMERIZATION of *isoprene,* $CH_2=CH\text{-}C(CH_3)=CH_2$. It was not possible, however, to use this direct method of synthesis, because large-scale supplies of isoprene were not available.

The Germans decided to use *dimethyl butadiene,* $CH_2=C(CH_3)-C(CH_3)=CH_2$, as the starting point, since it could be synthesized readily from the HYDROCARBON acetylene obtained from coal. The polymerization was carried out by warming the material to 158° F (70° C), and the process took three to six months to complete. The product was poor compared with natural rubber, but several thousand tons were produced and it was used for one of the toughest purposes to which rubber could be put, the manufacture of solid tires for wartime transportation.

After the war the process was improved by using metallic sodium as a CATALYST, to help in the reaction without itself taking part in it. The rubber made by this faster process was called *buna,* from the first syllable of butadiene and the chemical symbol for sodium, Na, which comes from its Latin name *natrium.* In the period between the World Wars natural rubber prices rose, but there was still only limited production of synthetic rubbers, mainly of types different from natural rubber. Some were resistant to solvents, oils and fats; others were capable of operating at temperatures significantly higher or lower than the range where natural rubber could be used.

Large-scale production

When World War II came, German interest in synthetic rubber for large-scale use was revived, especially for tires. The method of manufacture used was much more advanced than that of World War I.

A technique had been established for carrying out the polymerization in solution or emulsion form. The main component was *butadiene,* $CH_2=CH\text{-}CH=CH_2$, which is a gas at normal temperatures, but which liquefies readily under pressure. As butadiene alone did not give large enough polymer molecules, the molecular chain was loaded up by adding to it a second *monomer,* or building block, the AROMATIC COMPOUND *styrene,* $CH_2=CHC_6H_5$.

The reaction was encouraged by the addition of soaps, and catalysts were used, usually in the form of organic compounds of metals such as lithium. When, late in 1941, the Japanese overran Malaya and the Dutch East Indies, the western allies were

Left: An uncoagulated synthetic rubber latex being applied to the back of a carpet. It will eliminate the need for an underlay material. Right: Styrene Butadiene Rubber (SBR) is manufactured by polymerizing butadiene and styrene in the presence of a soap solution and a catalyst. The latex is coagulated, washed and dried, and then weighed into 80-lb (36-kg) bales, which are wrapped with polyethylene film.

THE PRODUCTION OF STYRENE BUTADIENE RUBBER (SBR)

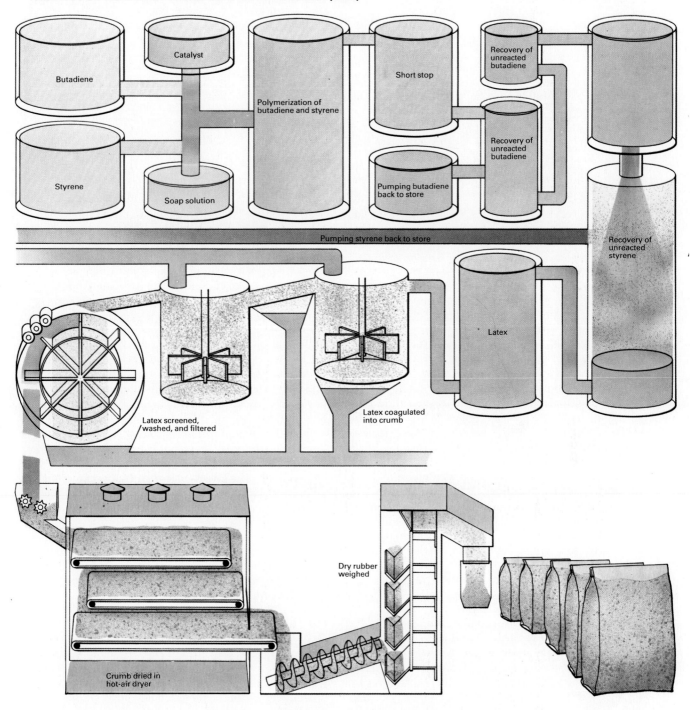

deprived in their turn of their main sources of natural rubber. At this stage large manufacturing units were rapidly set up in the U.S. to make synthetic rubber for truck and automobile tires, using the butadiene–styrene process.

As soon as a workable product was obtained, the process was standardized for the rest of the wartime emergency period. Large-scale production of a very uniform product was worked up, the butadiene coming from oil or alcohol, as available, and the styrene from coal. Deliveries began in 1942, and by 1943 the material was in widespread use. By the time of the defeat of Japan in 1945, production had reached a rate equivalent to a million tons a year.

For rubber tubes, it was found possible to make a synthetic rubber which had greatly improved air re-

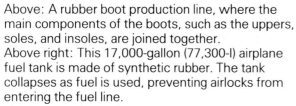

Above: A rubber boot production line, where the main components of the boots, such as the uppers, soles, and insoles, are joined together.
Above right: This 17,000-gallon (77,300-l) airplane fuel tank is made of synthetic rubber. The tank collapses as fuel is used, preventing airlocks from entering the fuel line.

tention, compared with natural rubber. This was called *butyl synthetic*, produced by polymerizing *isobutylene*, $CH_2=C(CH_3)_2$ (obtained from oil), with styrene. This material remains in use today as the standard rubber for tubes.

Modern synthetic rubber

At the end of the war, production of synthetic rubbers continued and rapid strides were made in the extension of the range to include a number of materials, with properties tailored to meet the needs of particular applications. Around 70 per cent of the rubber used is synthetic, with the largest single type being styrene-butadiene rubber (SBR) which is widely used in tire production.

In a typical modern process for producing styrene-butadiene rubber butadiene and styrene (typically in the ratio 70 per cent to 30 per cent) are first mixed with the catalyst and a soap solution and then fed to a polymerization reactor. When the reaction is complete, the product is treated to remove any unused butadiene and styrene, and the synthetic rubber *latex* is passed to a storage tank where it can be blended with other rubber compositions if desired. Next, the latex is coagulated to form crumbs which are dried in a hot air drier. Alteration of the processing conditions allows a range of different SBRs to be produced to suit various end uses.

The increased availability of isoprene has resulted in the development of a synthetic rubber which has the same general structure as natural rubber. The difficulty here is that the isoprene molecule is a three-dimensional structure which is capable of two forms of molecule. In natural rubber almost all the molecules are of one type, but in the synthetic variety both types are produced. However, by using *stereospecific* catalysts the microstructure of the rubber molecules can be controlled so that *cis*-1,4-polyisoprene is effectively a duplicate of natural rubber and can replace it for many applications.

One of the most important modern synthetic rubbers, *Neoprene,* is derived from polychloroprene, $CH_2=CH-CCl=CH_2$, and offers particularly good resistance to the effects of fire and solvents, together with high temperature stability. It also offers high tensile strength and abrasion resistance, and is widely used for conveyer belts.

Acrylonitrile rubber is made by polymerizing acrylonitrile, $CH_2=CHCN$, with butadiene. This also has excellent resistance to oil and organic solvents. *Polyurethane rubbers* contain the characteristic decimal linkage

$$-\overset{\overset{\textstyle H}{|}}{N}-\overset{\overset{\textstyle O}{||}}{C}-O-$$

and are used for rubber compounds of high mechanical strength and greater resistance to wear, for small solid tires with very high load capacities. It is also used as a base for the foam materials found in furniture and bedding. In *silicone rubbers,* the carbon backbone of a normal rubber is replaced by a chain of alternating silicon and oxygen atoms, and they are used in extremes of temperature.

See also: Hydrocarbon; Polymer and polymerization; Rubber, natural.

Rubik's cube

When Erno Rubik, a Hungarian lecturer on architecture and design, first created his magic cube, he had no idea of the impact it would have. He wanted simply to devise something that would help to develop three-dimensional perception in his students. Little did he realize that he was creating a puzzle that would perplex some of the world's most famous mathematicians, and bend the minds of young and old alike.

Rubik was not the only one to think of the idea. At roughly the same time, Terotoshi Ishige, a Japanese engineer, invented a puzzle based on the same principles. But it was Rubik's cube that first came to the public's attention, and it is he who is generally acknowledged as its inventor. Since that time the Rubik cube has developed into a huge multimillion-dollar industry which has spawned a number of similar products, such as the Worm, the Snake, and the Pyramid.

The Rubik Cube is deceptively simple. Each of its six faces is subdivided into a 3 × 3 array of nine facelets. Each vertical or horizontal layer in a face can be rotated around the center of the cube, giving the impression that the cube comprises 27 cubelets or *cubies* that seem to be able to move independently yet somehow remain held together, as if by magic. The commonest version of the cube comes with each of its six faces all one color – usually white, red, blue, orange, green, and yellow.

Restoring the cube to its original pristine state

RUBIK'S CUBE MECHANISM

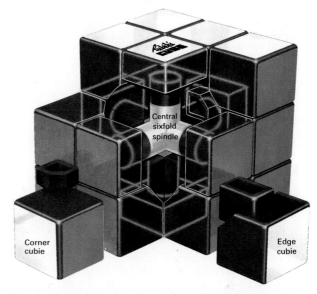

Above: One way to find out about Rubik's Cube is to take it apart, by a prizing force. At the heart of each cube is a spindle which holds the six central cubies in place. The rest of the cubies – another 14 – are held together by snap-fit hinges.

might then seem a fairly trivial matter, but minutes, or even hours, later it becomes clear that the Rubik Cube is not so simple. It may well take the beginner several days, if not weeks, of total dedication before he or she gets the cube back to its original state – or start position, as the cubologists call it.

Right: During manufacture, a Rubik Cube is colored with self-adhesive squares applied by hand – a job requiring extreme patience. The cube has six faces subdivided into nine facelets. Each face is a different color, usually white, red, blue, orange, green or yellow. This stage is the slowest of the production line.

ASSEMBLY AND DISASSEMBLY

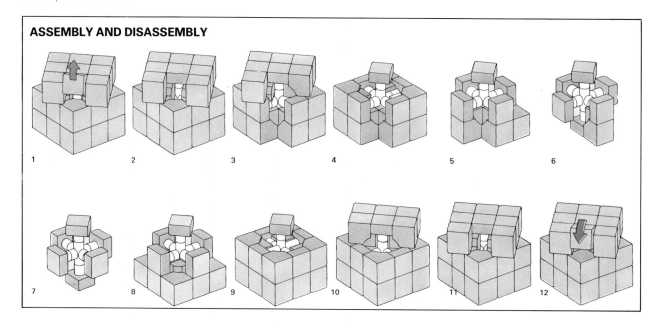

Above: Assembling and disassembling the Rubik Cube. To disassemble, first prize up the central edge cubie (1) to expose the inner mechanism (2) of the cube. Prize away the two nearest corner cubies (3) and remove the top layer, except for the fixed center cubie (4). Remove the three remaining corner cubies on the middle layer (5) and prize off the remaining cubies on the bottom layer (6). The disassembled cube (7). Reassembly is a reversal of the disassembly, replace the bottom layer first (8), then reassemble the middle layer (9). Assemble the back two rows on the top layer (10), then add the front two corner cubies (11). The final step is to squeeze the central edge cubie into place (12).

If you have a scrambled cube and you have given up trying to work out how to get back to start, your best bet is to take it apart to see how Rubik's ingenious mechanism works. To prize the cube apart without destroying it, turn one layer so that it is oriented diagonally with respect to the other two. Then, using a small screwdriver, carefully prize up one of the edge cubelets that form the central cross of the twisted layer.

Once you have pulled the whole cube apart you will find that it does not consist of 27 cubies, but rather of eight corner cubies, which have three faces, and 12 edge cubies with two faces. All have flanges that lock into the central mechanism, which consists of three spindles at right angles to each other. At the end of each spindle there is one face, which provides what appears as the center cubie of each of the six faces of the cube.

One of the best ways to learn how to unscramble a Rubik Cube is to start with a pristine cube and then experiment with it. It is also a way to learn something of the mathematics that the cube can demonstrate, as well as to improve your spatial awareness. But before you start it is best to have a notation system so that you can follow instructions, like a program, which allows you to keep track of what you are doing so that you can always backtrack to find out where you went wrong.

David Singmaster, a mathematician at the Polytechnic of the South Bank, London, who has done so much to promote the Rubik Cube, has devised a notation that is foolproof and can be easily adapted to similar puzzles. The six colors on an unscrambled cube can be arranged in various ways (30 in fact), so there is little point in referring to color. Instead, Singmaster suggests using up (U), down (D), front (F), back (B), right (R) and left (L) to define the faces.

To remember which is up and so on – which becomes difficult when you are twisting and turning layers through many moves – always choose the same colors to be up, left, etc. Remember that the central cubie of each face fixes the color of that face, because it is fixed to one of the three central spindles. So even when the cube appears scrambled you always know that the face with red at the center is left, the one with white at the center is up, and so on.

Start by rotating the face designated front clockwise by 90°, so the layer that was at the front of the up face moves to the front of the right face, and the layer that was at the front of left becomes the front of up, and so on. Singmaster's notation refers to this move, a clockwise rotation of the front face, as simply F. He defines clockwise rotation for all the faces in the same manner, but note that by clockwise he means clockwise when looking directly at any given face. If you are looking at the front face, the back face appears to turn counterclockwise when actually you turn it clockwise. The other way to turn each face is counterclockwise (again as viewed from the front of each face) and Singmaster uses dashes to indicate a counterclockwise rotation through 90° – for example, D′ means down in a counterclockwise direction.

Singmaster refers to twists of two opposite faces in opposition directions (clockwise and counterclockwise) as a slice movement (subscript *s*), because it is effectively the same as rotating the central slice. Remember that looking from the viewpoint of the front of one face these rotations will appear to be in the same direction. So, in Singmaster's notation U_s (up slice) refers to a clockwise twist of up and a counterclockwise twist of down, that is, UD′. Similarly, $R_s = RL'$ and F = FR′.

Pretty patterns

Once the basic notation system has been mastered, start to experiment. A number of pretty patterns can be achieved with slice moves only. For instance, there is the six-spot pattern which comes simply from $R_sF_sU_sR_s$, and a six-X pattern which is $R_sR_sF_sF_sU_sU_s$. A simpler way of writing down this second pattern is as $(R_s)^2 (F_s)^2 (U_s)^2$, where $(R_s)^2$ means that you do R_s twice, which actually means rotating the faces through twice 90°, or 180°.

Another group of Rubik's cube patterns that you can investigate is the antislice group. An antislice move consists of turning two opposite layers in a clockwise direction. A convenient shorthand for the antislice move is to use the subscript *a*, so F_a = FB, R_a = RL and U_a = UD. Moving two opposite layers counterclockwise gives you the inverse members of

Above: An unscrambled cube – the start and finish position; each side is a different color.

the group, as with $R'_a = R'L'$, and so on.

The notation system, once it has been mastered, allows you to investigate moves that are useful in developing a system, or *algorithm,* for returning a cube to start from a scrambled state. There are

Right: A prototype Rubik cube. The first examples were made of wood and had symbols instead of colored squares. Originally designed to develop three-dimensional perception in design students, the cube is a puzzle that has perplexed some of the world's most eminent mathematicians.

Left: A completely disassembled Rubik Cube. Below: Basic moves and solutions. (A) and (B): correctly orienting the cube. (C) to (G): some basic moves and their notations. (H) to (J): three slice moves – twists of two opposite faces in opposite directions. (K): a number of patterns, can be achieved with slice moves only. (L): an essential starting point for developing an algorithm is to make sure that the cube is arranged so that each central, fixed cubie is correctly placed relative to the others. (M) to (P): two ways of flipping an edge cubie from the top layer to the central layer, without unscrambling the rest of the cube. If the piece you want to be in the middle layer is in the upper layer, rotate up so that this piece is at the center of the upper layer of the front face, and the position to which it is to move is at the right of the middle layer of the front face. If the upper face of this piece matches the color of the front face of the cube, then you perform $F/U^2L/ULU^2F$. This moves uf to fr (and fr to lu). If, on the other hand, the front of the piece matches the front of the cube, then perform LF^2UFU/F^2L, moving fu to fr.

Both these moves allow you to unscramble the middle layer.

BASIC MOVES AND SOLUTIONS

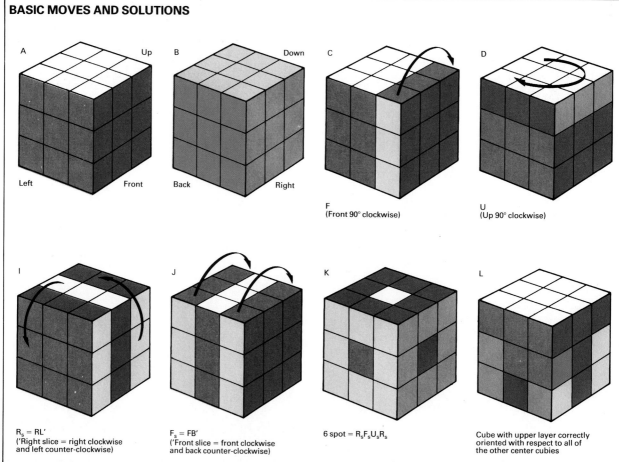

A Up
Left Front

B Down
Back Right

C
F
(Front 90° clockwise)

D
U
(Up 90° clockwise)

I
$R_s = RL'$
('Right slice = right clockwise and left counter-clockwise)

J
$F_s = FB'$
('Front slice = front clockwise and back counter-clockwise)

K
6 spot = $R_sF_sU_sR_s$

L
Cube with upper layer correctly oriented with respect to all of the other center cubies

many ways to unscramble a cube, and experts have their own preferred algorithms. Morwen Thistlethwaite, a colleague of Singmaster, has used a computer to show that it is possible to return to start in 52 moves, and he thinks that he might be able to reduce this to 45 moves. The mathematical theory of groups suggests that it should be possible to solve the Rubik Cube in as few as 22 or 23 moves, although no one has evolved such an efficient solution, and most people take well over 100 moves.

Scrambling while unscrambling

Most algorithms involve unscrambling one layer of the cube at a time (although in the process you may appear to rescramble the cube on many occasions). The crucial point to remember is that the center cubie of each face defines the color of that face. With that knowledge it is easy to work out where each cubie should be – although moving the cubie to where you want it is not quite so simple.

Once two layers are positioned correctly, you need to be able to move pieces around in the third layer without scrambling the two layers you have just sorted out.

Encouraged by the success of the Rubik Cube,

manufacturers have produced a number of other similar puzzles. These come in various shapes and sizes – and some use colored balls instead of cubies – but they all work on the same principle as the cube.

With a little effort, it should be possible to adapt Singmaster's standard notation system to each of these puzzles and use it to work out an algorithm – or series of algorithms – for each puzzle.

Racing cubes

To achieve speed, cube-solving competitors use a carefully worked-out algorithm – or better still, a number of different algorithms suited to the state in which they find the scrambled cube. Most competitiors are not beyond a little cunning to help them to win. For instance, they may take the cube apart at regular intervals to lubricate the mechanism so it responds to the slightest twitch of the competitor's fingers.

Learning to solve the Rubik Cube or one of its derivatives can take a long time. But the notation system at least gives a chance to retrace the steps and see what went wrong.

See also: Computer; Cryptology; Mathematics.

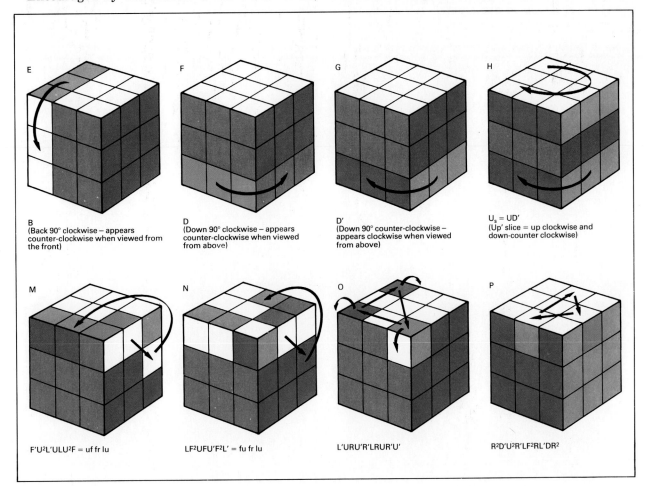

E
B
(Back 90° clockwise – appears counter-clockwise when viewed from the front)

F
D
(Down 90° clockwise – appears counter-clockwise when viewed from above)

G
D'
(Down 90° counter-clockwise – appears clockwise when viewed from above)

H
U_s = UD'
(Up' slice = up clockwise and down-counter clockwise)

M
F'U²L'ULU²F = uf fr lu

N
LF²UFU'F²L' = fu fr lu

O
L'URU'R'LRUR'U'

P
R²D'U²R'LF²RL'DR²

Rudder

The earliest form of rudder was simply an oar or paddle which was used to propel the stern of the ship in a sideways direction. Later, the paddle was secured to the side of the ship and provided with a lever at the upper end of its handle to act as a tiller. It is not known with certainty when the first stern post rudder was invented, but it was in general use in the twelfth century AD.

Rudder action

The passage of a ship through the water causes water to flow past the rudder, and the angle at which the rudder is inclined to the direction of flow is called the *angle of attack*. The steering action is dependent on the pressure distribution between the two hydrodynamic surfaces of the rudder. The pressure on the downstream side is less than the *static pressure* of the surrounding water, while the pressure on the upstream side is greater. The result of this is an outward force on the downstream side of the rudder, and this can be regarded as being made up of a *lift force* at right angles to the direction of flow, and a *drag force* directly opposing the direction of flow. The variation of the lift and drag forces for different angles of attack is extremely important in rudder design as it is the lift force which creates the turning effect. At a certain angle of attack, called the *critical angle,* the rudder *stalls:* a phenomenon called *burbling* occurs and the rudder force is sudenly reduced. Burbling is caused by a breakdown in the streamlined flow on the downstream side of the rudder into a swirling irregular *eddying flow*. Rudders on merchant vessels are normally expected to operate up to an angle of 35 degrees from the centerline to port or starboard, and so the critical angle is important as a reduction of rudder force would be undesirable within the working range.

Results from model tests with rudders in open water must be interpreted with care and cannot be directly applied to a ship as the rudder action is modified by the flow of water around the hull interacting with the *propeller slip*. Reliable results can only be obtained from fullscale ship tests, and then the model information must be corrected by a suitable factor for further rudder design.

When a ship's rudder is turned, the ship first moves a small distance sideways in the opposite direction to the intended turn and then moves around a circular path until it eventually faces the opposite direction. The distance moved forward from the point at which the rudder was turned to the point at

Left: The rudder of a ship is located directly behind the propeller. Its surfaces are designed to give maximum turning force and minimum resistance to water flow. On merchant ships, the rudder is normally expected to operate at angles of up to 35 degrees from the centerline to port or starboard, so the critical angle – the angle of attack at which the rudder force is suddenly reduced – is important. A reduction of force within the working range could be disastrous, especially if the ship is maneuvering in a harbor, or in crowded shipping lanes.

which the ship is at right angles to its original direction is called the *advance*. *Transfer* is the sideways distance between these two points, and the diameter of the circular path followed by the ship is called the *tactical diameter*. During the turn the bow of the vessel lies always inside the turning curve, so that a *drift angle* is formed between the center line of the vessel and the tangent to the turning curve. The tactical diameter is a measure of the ability of the rudder to turn the vessel. It is important for warships, because they frequently execute complicated turning maneuvers.

Right: A fabricated rudder for a modern single-propeller vessel. In most large vessels, the rudder is turned by hydraulic or electric machinery, which is powered from the engine room and controlled from the bridge.

Below: The Navyflux thruster steers the ship by driving water out on either side of the vessel. An axial pump is mounted in the front limb of the tunnel, so this type of thruster does not require forward motion of the ship to operate. At high forward speeds, it will steer the ship even when the pump is not running.

Rudder design

With a simple rudder arranged to turn around the edge nearest the ship, the force produced by the rudder will act to return the rudder to the straight ahead position, and this force has to be resisted by the steering gear to maintain the turn. To avoid excessive steering forces a *balanced* rudder arrangement is employed with the turning axis being positioned some way along the rudder near to the center of pressure of the turning forces. In a semi-balanced rudder the proportion of the rudder area in front of the turning axis is 20 per cent or less,

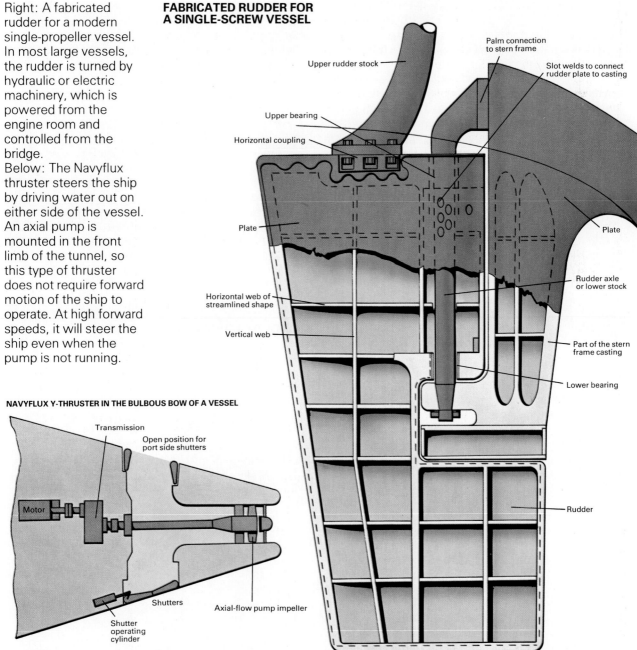

FABRICATED RUDDER FOR A SINGLE-SCREW VESSEL

- Upper rudder stock
- Palm connection to stern frame
- Slot welds to connect rudder plate to casting
- Upper bearing
- Horizontal coupling
- Plate
- Plate
- Horizontal web of streamlined shape
- Rudder axle or lower stock
- Vertical web
- Part of the stern frame casting
- Lower bearing
- Rudder

NAVYFLUX Y-THRUSTER IN THE BULBOUS BOW OF A VESSEL

- Transmission
- Open position for port side shutters
- Motor
- Shutters
- Shutter operating cylinder
- Axial-flow pump impeller

PLAN VIEW OF JET-FLAP RUDDER

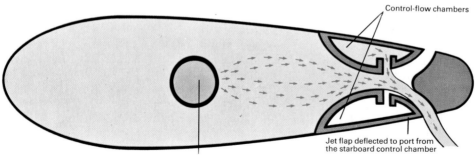

Control-flow chambers

Main flow and control through rudder stock

Jet flap deflected to port from the starboard control chamber

Left: In a jet-flap rudder, water is pumped in through the upper stock (the rudder turning linkage) and leaves through a vertical slot near to the trailing edge. The main jet of water emerging from this slot can be switched to the left or right by means of a control chamber, which is also fed with water from the upper stock.

whereas for a fully balanced design the value will be 25 to 30 per cent.

A number of different arrangements are used to support the rudder and allow it to turn with most using tapered pintles working in bearings. These bearings are often water lubricated, although oil lubrication is also used. In some cases all the support is provided by the upper bearing on the ship's hull and in others there is a lower bearing beneath the rudder. The turning motion is provided by the *rudder stock* which is made from cast or forged steel and bolted to the rudder. The upper end of the stock passes into the ship's hull through a trunk with a watertight seal and is connected to the steering gear. Normally the steering gear is power operated with the stock being turned by hydraulic rams supplied with oil from electric pumps and controlled from the steering position on the bridge. The rudder itself is generally made from steel plate with the sides being stiffened by internal webs or a cast frame. A drain hole is provided, but in some designs the interior of the rudder may be foam-filled.

Rudder types

Many different designs of rudder have been developed, with the simplest being the *fully movable* type where the whole rudder moves as one unit. A development of the fully movable design is the Schilling rudder which has a special hydrodynamic profile and is fitted with upper and lower plates to guide the water flow. These modifications result in an increased deflection of the water flow from the propeller (which is immediately in front of the rudder), giving a rapid response and increased maneuverability, and allowing a vessel to turn in its own length when starting from rest.

Another design suitable for vessels that have to be highly maneuverable, such as ferry boats, fishing vessels and offshore supply boats, is the Becker, or *articulated,* rudder. It consists of a main rudder of conventional profile with a pivoted fin mounted on the rear edge. A pivoting mechanism turns the fin

through an angle around twice that of the main rudder to increase the deflection of the water flow. At low speeds the articulated rudder produces a greater force and so a more positive turning effect. Somewhat similar is the *flapped rudder,* though in this case the movable flap on the trailing edge of the main rudder is operated by hydraulic rams within the main rudder. Minor steering corrections under way can be carried out by use of the flap alone, while with the flap set centrally the complete unit acts as a conventional rudder.

An *active rudder* has a propulsion unit fitted into the rudder body and a fixed or variable pitch propeller at its trailing edge. When the rudder is turned, the propeller will produce thrust at an angle to the center line of the vessel, causing a greater turning effect than the rudder alone. To operate, the rudder is not dependent on the forward motion of the ship.

Other steering systems

A *water jet unit* may be used for propulsion and steering. The system is extremely useful for ferries and river craft where maneuvering in confined waters is essential. Water is drawn into the unit and then discharged at high speed through a set of vanes which can be rotated to give thrust in any direction. Two units may be fitted to a vessel, one forward and one aft, to give maximum turning effect.

A *bow thrust unit* consists of a water tunnel at right angles to the center line of a ship, fitted with a PROPELLER whose *blade angle* or *pitch* can be varied by a hydraulic control. By altering the pitch, the amount of thrust can be adjusted to give the required lateral movement of the ship. The unit is controlled from the bridge of the vessel and the propeller is driven by a motor through a flexible connection and bevel gearing. Bow thrusters are used on many ships, such as oil tankers, bulk carriers and passenger vessels, and they are used for accurate course control for cable laying vessels.

See also: Propeller, marine; Ship; Warship.

Safe

Safes are designed to be secure not only from burglars but from natural disasters such as fires and flooding. Some safes survived the Chicago fire of 1871, after falling through burning buildings, but the survival of the safe does not mean the survival of its contents if the safe is warped by heat.

In the U.S., safes are tested by prolonged exposure to heat and by dropping them from heights, and divided into categories according to the protection they offer: record safes offer protection from fire, money safes from burglars, and the third category comprises a money safe inside a record safe.

Construction

Safes used to be made of *case-hardened* steel but carbide-tipped drills were soon developed which could cut through it. Today steel alloys are used which cannot be penetrated by drills; in addition, solid hardened particles are mixed in the steel during its molten state. Trying to drill such a plate results in stress which will chip or shatter the tip of a drill. The steel plates are made three layers thick, comprising a sandwich of hard steel alloy, seam welded all the way round to make a single structure, with a layer of a hard, fireproof composite material in the center to prevent the successful use of oxygen flame-cutting equipment. Some safes are cast in a single piece so there are no seams.

Locks

The lock of a burglarproof safe is nearly always a combination lock, because there is no keyhole into which explosives or lock-picking tools can be inserted, and because a four-ring lock, for example, offers more than 100,000,000 possible combinations. Also, the combination can be changed at the convenience of the safe's owner.

When locked, the door of the safe must fit as snugly as possible all the way round its edge. Consequently there are many bolts around the edge of the door. In the past, these bolts were all thrown by the lock and were only as secure as the lock itself; the safecracker's technique was to knock off the outside of the lock and drive out the spindle. Modern safes, however, have a mechanism in the lock which breaks the connection between the lock and the bolts when the lock is upset by heat or tools.

Lock mechanisms are protected by additional layers of drill-resistant steel, by key-operated dial-check locks which prevent unauthorized manipulation with the combination, and by anti-observation shields which make it difficult to observe the combination being dialed.

During a wave of bank robberies in the U.S. before World War II, time-lock devices began to be used, with which the combination lock cannot be opened during certain hours, making it pointless to kidnap or torture bank employees to make them reveal combinations. Combination locks are also fitted with a device which transmits an alarm to police if the dial is turned after business hours.

Vaults

A vault is a room, usually below ground, which is protected in much the same way as a safe. (Vault originally meant a room with a vaulted ceiling.) Vaults in Hiroshima survived the atomic blast there in 1945, only 300 yards (274 m) from the point below the explosion.

Vault doors are often round, because it is easier to achieve a perfect fit between two circles than two rectangles. The edge of the door is tapered to fit into a concave surface in the doorway. Vault doors are typically about 3.5 in. (90 mm) thick; the doors at Hiroshima were 6 in. (150 mm) thick.

See also: Lock, security; Steel manufacture.

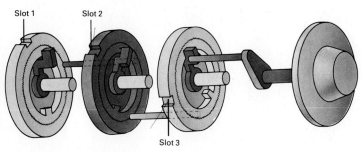

Slot 1　　Slot 2

Slot 3

Left: A typical office safe must be able to resist threats from various sources, including fire, flood, high-speed electric drills, oxyacetylene torches and high explosives, if it is to be considered really secure.
Above: The mechanism of a combination lock. The slots must be aligned before the safe door can be opened.

Sailboard

Sailboarding is a complex sport stemming from the simple idea of attaching a mast and a sail to a surfboard. The emerging sport has needed a range of new skills, designs and materials to be developed. As the sport becomes established, designs have become standardized and sailboarding's continuing popularity seems assured, especially since its acceptance as an Olympic sport in 1984.

The first steerable sailboard was invented by Newman Darby in 1964, but the shape of the craft had more in common with conventional boats than the boards familiar today. A diamond-shaped sail was used, attached top and bottom to the mast. Steering of the board was accomplished by inclining the sail fore and aft.

Hoyle Schweitzer and Jim Drake finally produced the familiar sailboard in 1969. Their original sailboard consisted of a normal surfboard, with a triangular sail attached to a mast and stretched with a wishbone-shaped boom. Surfers steer their boards with movements of their bodies as motorcyclists partially steer their bikes, while dinghies can be influenced in their direction merely by the position of their sails. In the two separate principles lay the keys to the new sport.

Steering

Where the sailboard crosses the boundary between surfboard and dinghy is in its movable mast. Slotted into the board around the center point (some boards have two mast slots), the mast is held in place by a universal joint. The sailor hangs onto the wish-boom; there are no stays. The universal joint allows the sailor to move the mast fore or aft at will and this, combined with movements of the body, is all the control a boardsailor has.

Whether the board *luffs up* – steers into the wind – or *bears away* – steers away from the wind – is governed by the relationship between the board's center of effort and the *daggerboard's* central point of lateral resistance.

The center of effort is the notional center of all the wind force upon the sail, the location of this point varying with the wind's angle of attack. With the

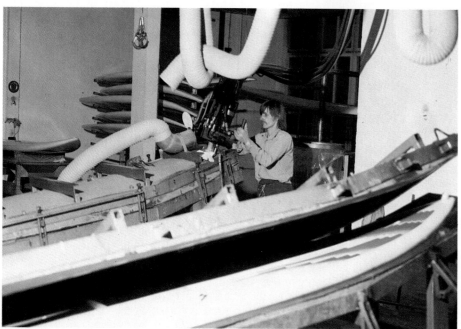

Left: An ultralight foam is injected into the hull of a sailboard during manufacture.
Above: The outer shell of the sailboard is made of polycarbonate sheet and low-friction Makrolon. It is lined with a layer of carbon-reinforced glass fiber to provide stiffness, a layer of high-density polyurethane to provide structural stability, and a polyester mat layer. The foam is injected under pressure.

Above: The Klepper 320 sailboard has a number of features that make it particularly suitable for high-performance sailing in strong winds.

sail tilted forward, the center of effort moves forward of the center of lateral resistance and the board bears away. With the center of effort behind the center of lateral resistance, the board luffs up.

Once the basic art of steering is mastered the sailboarder is ready to utilize the wishboom fully by tacking (changing direction), a natural extension of steering. Tacking requires manual dexterity combined with physical agility and these are prerequisites for a successful boardsailor. As the board points into the wind, the sail empties and flutters, bringing the board to a gradual halt if the tack is not executed quickly enough. At this point, the sailor simply walks around the front of the mast, grabs hold of the other side of the wishboom and tilts the mast backward to bear away in the new direction. Such are the gymnastic skills that are required of an accomplished sailboarder.

Board design

There is a wide variety of sailboard designs. In many respects the sailboard is a water wing (Jim Drake was an aeronautical designer) except that the water traverses its length longitudinally. One of the most frequently used materials in board manufacture is polyethylene; it is resilient and ideally suited to withstanding the rigors of sun, sea and hard use. In the early days, polyethylene did much to promote the use of sailboards. Du Pont, the material's manufacturer, gave sailboards extensive publicity for novel use of a material that was more commonly used to make Frisbees. Kevlar is also used to make sailboards. The material is five times stronger than steel without the metal's weight, but is also extremely expensive.

With their closed-cell construction all boards are fully buoyant even if punctured by rocks. But for efficiency they must be shaped to offer the least area to the sea (wetted area) and be equipped with a daggerboard to provide the lateral resistance essential when sailing into the wind. At the rear of the board a *skeg* (fin), similar to that used on surfboards and analogous to the dinghy's rudder, is used to provide directional stability. Without it even the most experienced sailboarder would find directional control difficult, with the board's rear end fishtailing from side to side, slowing progress drastically.

Since the development of the early boards, much thought and effort have been expended not only to improve the basic design but to produce a series of different designs suited to particular types of sailing. Boards used for regatta sailing have a deep hull similar to a dinghy's, and those used for wave jumping feature a distinctly upturned nose.

The design of the board's underside is a subject of much debate. Generally, boards built with accen-

STEERING THE BOARD

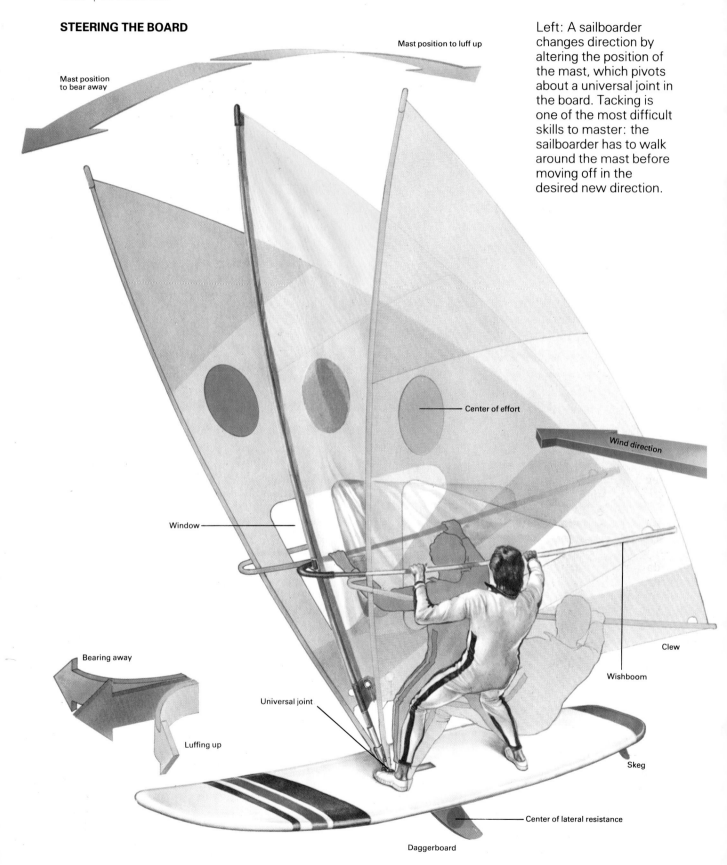

Mast position to luff up

Mast position to bear away

Left: A sailboarder changes direction by altering the position of the mast, which pivots about a universal joint in the board. Tacking is one of the most difficult skills to master: the sailboarder has to walk around the mast before moving off in the desired new direction.

Center of effort

Wind direction

Window

Clew

Bearing away

Wishboom

Universal joint

Luffing up

Skeg

Center of lateral resistance

Daggerboard

tuated *rocker* (the curvature from stem to stern) give high performance but some people may demand greater stability. Other board shapes have originated from studies of fluid mechanics. The Zeta's shape was first studied by two Australian scientists; its convex vee at the front aids progress through the water while toward the rear of the board this shape is gently inverted for stability and to generate lift, planing being one of the most exhilarating points of board sailing.

Soft boards

While the 46 lb (21 kg) Zeta board is constructed from glass-reinforced plastic with a foam filling, a new generation of boards has recently been introduced to add another dimension to the sport. Soft boards like the Goolie and Windjammer make no compromises on strength or rigidity yet are produced with a weight of just 26 lb (12 kg), half the weight of conventional boards. The soft polyethylene foam hulls allow sailors to dig their toes in for good grip and ample control. This combined with the board's light weight, which requires less kinetic energy to launch it into the air, makes it ideal for wave jumping and acrobatic free-style sailing. Its pedigree is impressive. The Windjammer was developed in California and Hawaii, two of the best areas for waves in the world, but although it is ideal for these conditions, it remains suitable for the beginner, because of the high degree of security and control it affords.

Skegs, singly or paired, follow a basic line of construction and use, though different shapes are available (generally smaller) for those willing to sacrifice a little directional stability in favor of less turbulence beneath the board. There is more scope for variety in the construction of the daggerboard. Racing daggerboards, adjusted by foot, rely on the boardsailor's ability and offer minimum turbulence around the board. They are usually aided by a daggerboard gasket consisting simply of a neoprene (synthetic rubber) strip attached to the daggerboard slot with a petroleum-based contact adhesive.

The sailboarding novice, however, requires the maximum lateral resistance in order to make the board easier to control. Shorter and more robust than the racing daggerboard, the school board has more of the stormboard's qualities – strength and rigidity under all conditions.

The mast

The unstable appearance of a sailboard at sea is not improved by its mast swaying wildly under the wind's influence. However, precarious though it may look, this system is essential to the sailboard's stability. The universal joint about which the mast pivots is one of the most important features of the whole board, being not only vital to its performance

but also to the safety of the sailor. Essentially one of two types, the joint or pivot will be either purely mechanical, where the mast is fixed to it with a pin, or it will be one of the flexible types made of a resilient rubber or nylon.

For control, it is essential for the mast and board to remain connected and, as the pivot is the medium for this, its condition is of paramount importance. Positioned firmly while sailing, the pivot must be able to be pulled free in an emergency so as not to trap the sailor in the event of an overturn. Given the right equipment, fatalities are few in board sailing, but in foul weather the mast coming adrift will lead to certain disaster. The Panther system board pivot is unique in its design, achieving the balance between firm location and easy extraction by using a suction device. The mast is simply plugged into a deck socket incorporating a simple suction washer. Even if a board sailor loses control only the mast and sail will lie in the water along the lines of a dinghy capsize. Once back on the board, the sailor can easily right the mast with a tug on the *uphaul*, a sheet (rope) attached to the mast for this purpose.

Most sailboards have a mast about 14.75 ft (4.5 m) long. Glass fiber, aluminum (18 gauge, anodized for salt water protection) and alloy are the most popular materials. An aluminum mast is about 7 lb (3 kg) in weight. These materials allow the mast to flex a little in strong winds, or else the mast would most likely snap, but an excessively flexible mast would result in significant power losses. Carbon fiber is sometimes used because of its great strength and light weight. It is expensive, however, and many competitors are opposed to its use, arguing that it is against the amateur spirit of the sport.

Metal masts are usually one-piece constructions with parallel sides. Glass fiber masts, on the other hand, are usually tapered. Although the thinner top makes the mast less strong it can lend a beneficial whiplash effect. Glass fiber masts are usually used with all-purpose boards.

The wishboom

Though a good mast can make all the difference between an empty and a full sail, it is basically the skill of the sailor using the wishboom that insures good speed through the water. The wishboom, so named because of its appearance, is the brake, accelerator and tiller of the sailboard. Unlike a dinghy, the wishboom completely encircles the sail; the sailor controls the board by grasping one side of the boom or the other depending upon which tack he or she is on. Grip is an essential feature of the wishboom; a slip of the hand easily leads to complete loss of control, so the aluminum bars are rubber sleeved and shaped to be within reach in all conditions. At 7 lb (3 kg), the wishboom presents few problems to the sailor, being light enough to allow freestyle tricks to be exploited once the basics have been mastered.

The sail

Completing the rigging triangle is the sail. The sail's design depends on its purpose. Wave jumpers and those who like heavy-weather sailing look for strength while those seeking to exploit light winds in a race will look for the flexibility necessary to make full use of the merest hint of a breeze. Sail area ranges from about 59 to 70 sq ft (5.5 to 6.5 sq m). Most sailors need a set of each of these sizes to be equipped for the conditions they will encounter.

Above: A selection of sailboard fins, made of glass-filled polycarbonate for strength and stiffness. Like a dinghy's rudder, the sailboard fin is used to provide directional stability.

Sails of less area (45 sq ft) are often used where there is plenty of wind whereas *high-aspect* Hawaiian storm sails present something of a paradox. Designed for use where wind is abundant, the storm sail is made over-size to compensate for the blanking effect encountered when a board is at the bottom of a deep wave trough. Cut with a higher *clew* (the eyelet used to secure the sail to the end of the boom) than is usual in order to prevent the wishboom end from catching on wave walls, the

Left: Even if the sailboarder loses control and lets go of the wishboom, only the sail and mast fall into the water, because of the universal joint connecting the mast to the board. The sailboarder rights the mast and sail simply by pulling on the uphaul, the rope attached to the mast specifically for this purpose.

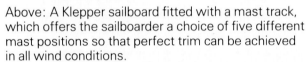

Above: A Klepper sailboard fitted with a mast track, which offers the sailboarder a choice of five different mast positions so that perfect trim can be achieved in all wind conditions.

Above: Wave jumping is one of many variations on board sailing. It requires a strong, light board, as well as great skill and the correct wind and wave conditions.

Hawaiian sail is good for adult novices too, owing to its large wind-catching area.

The diversity in board sailing is vast. Freestyle, wave jumping, racing and long distance are all forms of the sport practiced with ever-growing popularity. Long-distance sailing has led to the interesting development of a vario-sail. Forced by the lack of a conventional boom about which to reef the sail in an adverse weather change, designers turned to the zipper to provide them with a previously unforeseen flexibility. Now sections can be added or removed at will.

Materials used in board sails vary to the same extent as in dinghy sailing but resilience and strength are two prime qualities sought by the sailmaker. ICI's Terylene sailcloth dominates, with windows set into the sail to provide visibility.

As in any sport or realm of technological development, factions form and split away from others. In sailboarding the result is that many different types of board and of sailing now exist, rapidly forcing the pace of development. The original Windsurfer was quickly followed by the Winglider and Mistral boards. The Winglider scored buoyancy and weight points, and thus speed, over the Windsurfer but the European licensees of the Windsurfer responded with their TC39 hull – a V-shape with impressive upwind performance.

In search of speed
The quest for speed advanced even further with the introduction of the semi-displacement hull. Borrowing heavily from dinghy design, its speed was almost entirely derived from its hull shape but it was a board for the experienced sailor – less than a dozen of Europe's top sailors are able to compete effectively with this more radical design. The Open meetings where these boards may be raced bristle with innovation. The 65 sq ft (6 sq m) sails are controlled by pulley systems attached to the wishboom while straps may be used to adjust the tension of the sail's foot and trailing edge. Other innovations such as tapered racing battens (inserted into the sail's *leech,* or trailing edge, to control shape) once again are taken from dinghy experience.

Not all sailboarding is about course racing, however. In 1976 speeds of 10 knots were thought impossible but, in 1977, Derek Thijs confounded the critics with a speed of over 19 knots in the 107 sq ft (10 sq m) sail class. Since then speeds have increased, with the fastest speed standing at 38.2 knots – a good speed for any wind-powered craft.

Record setting should be aided by the proposal for a new system of electronic timing shared between the timekeepers and the official observers based on shore. Shore-based timekeepers will be in direct radio link with officials at the start and finish of the course and the new equipment will incorporate a print-out and a microcomputer so that if a competitor is close to setting a new world record, the information can be relayed quickly to take advantage of the prevailing weather conditions.

See also: Sailing technology; Wave motion.

Sailing technology

The history of people's ability to keep themselves and goods afloat on boats must go back many tens of thousands of years, and these earliest logs, bundles of reeds or branches, could travel only where water currents or primitive paddles allowed. After the discovery of paddles it would soon have become obvious that the wind could be as powerful an opponent to muscular propulsion as could be the currents and waves, so frequently forcing an undesirable drift to leeward. That humans learned fairly early to use this drift to advantage is clear from vase paintings and clay models of Egyptian origin, variously dated by archaeologists to be 7000 to 11,000 years old. Certainly by 3000 BC this controlled drifting, or downwind sailing, using large square-shaped sails, was a firmly established seagoing technique for the transport of people and goods.

From the details of reliefs depicting these vessels we can deduce that the sails were hung from a horizontal spar *yard* which could be set at different ang-les to the wind by means of ropes attached to its end. The square shape is obviously consistent with the earliest technologies of woven fiber or reed, it can be easily hung, raised or furled onto a simple spar, and when controlled by ties from its corners it is naturally blown by the wind into a near optimum curvature for downwind sailing, also allowing some angular variation from this course.

As in the much quicker development of modern fuel-driven transport devices, the technological development of sailing vessels has always been a compromise between demands for speed, cargo-carrying capacity and maneuverability, qualities which due to the complexity of their interaction and to local traditions and available materials throughout the world have led to the building of a tremendous variety of boats – by no means all successful.

The next important ability of a sailboat, after that of sailing fast downwind, is the ability to sail at angles departing from the downwind direction, and the greater this angle the greater will be the period of the voyage when wind can be used and the oars put away. Thus an exceedingly important stage of

Below left and right: Two competitors in the Antigua Race Week. Before the event, the crews would have practiced extensively to bring the boats and rigging to peak trim. Below: A hull passing through water generates side forces at right angles to the curvature of the surface. These forces can be considered as a single resultant acting at one point.

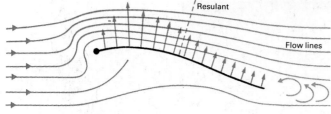

Resulant

Flow lines

this development is when a boat becomes capable of sailing reliably at 90 degrees to the wind direction and so *holding station*. This achieved, the crew is completely independent of oars, whatever the wind direction, because it is always possible to sail to any destination by holding station during periods of unfavorable winds, oars only being required for extreme wave conditions and inshore navigation. Longer journeys would also become more acceptable as knowledge of the large-scale circulations of wind over ocean surfaces increased, enabling routes to be picked which involved holding station less time.

Windward sailing

Gradually boats achieved the capability of sailing slightly into wind, a feature so contrary to intuition that it is not surprising that the associated technology seems to have been learned, lost and rediscovered many times and by many apparently well-separated societies, even though this ability itself might be considered to be the best method for its distribution. This only reflects the heavy overlay of tradition in sailing vessel construction. A success in some detail, once achieved, was held firmly in local collective memory to such an extent that it often inhibited, or made impossible, the incorporation of

further improvements. The advantages of sailing closer into the eye of the wind are considerable; to be able to sail closer than a trading adversary often insures the quickest delivery of cargo, or a wartime adversary can often be outmaneuvered or eluded irrespective of his possible weapon superiority.

It is impossible for a boat with normal sails to sail directly into the wind. It is possible, however, to sail along a line at right angles to the wind direction (*reaching*) by setting the sail closer to the center line of the boat, rather than across it; it is easier for the boat to move through the water in the direction it is pointing, rather than sideways, so the result is that it moves at right angles to the wind. If the rudder is set so as to continually point the boat further into the wind, it is then possible to sail even closer to the wind direction. To progress into the wind, a series of paths at an angle to the wind are followed first one way then the other, always getting a little further upwind. This procedure is called *beating*.

The special design features required for good windward sailing were only being realized in the nineteenth century and the racing yachts of today have windward performances well exceeding the fast clippers of the 1850 period, although their maximum speed when reaching at 90 degrees to the wind is only slightly superior. These special features are those associated with *side forces* at least as much as with the *drag forces* most important in downwind sailing.

Imagine a boat sailing close to the wind – that is, pointing to within about 45 degrees of the wind direction. There are various forces on the sail and on the hull which can be split up into components in

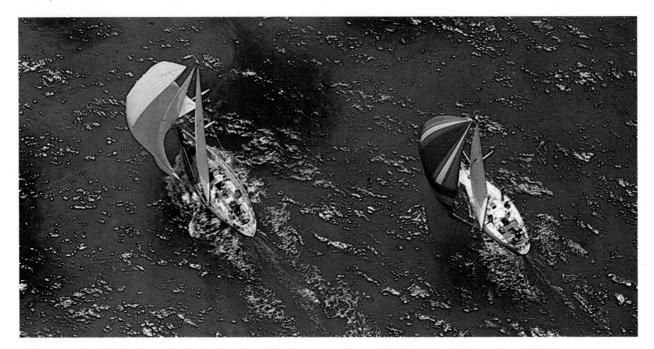

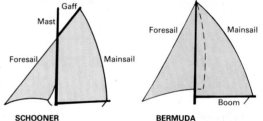

Above: High-speed racing yachts with sails of light, strong synthetic fiber.
Right: A Schooner and a Bermuda rigging. In the Schooner the foresail was sharpened by replacing the oblique yard with a permanently set luff and suspending the mainsail on the aft portion of the yard. The need to reduce topside weight led to the Schooner rigging being superseded by the Bermuda.
Below right: This crank is used to hoist the mainsail while the mainsail boom can be turned to reef.

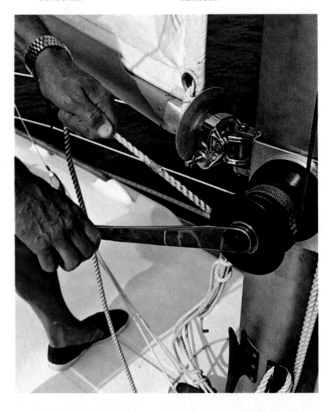

each direction. In each case, the side force is that force acting perpendicular to the flow of either air or water, and the drag force is that acting along the flow. In each case these forces have a combined *resultant*. The side force on the sails and the side force on the hull act in opposite directions because the wind is blowing on the sail, but the water is resisting the sideways movement of the hull.

For successful sailing into the wind, the ratio of side forces to drag forces must be a maximum, for both the aerodynamic forces acting on the sail rigging, and also for the hydrodynamic forces acting on the hull. That is, the side forces should be as large as possible compared with their respective drag forces.

When a sailboat is in a steady sailing condition, the resultant aerodynamic and hydrodynamic forces must balance each other out completely. Therefore another way of stating the special conditions required for good windward sailing is that the drag angle of the sail (ϵ) and the drag angle of hull (δ) must each be as small as possible because, as the diagram shows, the angle of sailing into the wind is equal to the sum of ϵ and δ. As this sum decreases, so the boat can sail closer into the wind.

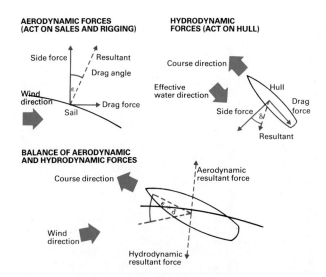

AERODYNAMIC FORCES (ACT ON SALES AND RIGGING)

HYDRODYNAMIC FORCES (ACT ON HULL)

BALANCE OF AERODYNAMIC AND HYDRODYNAMIC FORCES

Above: A yacht sailing at about 45° into the wind will have an aerodynamic side force acting at 90° to the wind, and a drag force along the direction of flow. Similarly, hydrodynamic side forces and drag forces act on the hull. The resultant hydrostatic and aerodynamic forces are balanced. The net effect is a driving force into the wind.
Right: A computer-controlled propulsion system.

Origin of forces

The drag force results from the fluid particles being slowed by the object itself, the drag being less as the shape is slimmer, rounded-off, or streamlined and its surface is smoothed. The side force (or *lift* in the case of aircraft) depends subtly on the curvature and thickness of the shape, which is similar to an airfoil. The high values of side force coupled with low drag force required by a sail for good windward performance demand thin spars and rigging, a stiff forward edge (*luff*) and a small curvature (*camber*) so that the shape is not destroyed when used at the low angles of wind incidence demanded for windward working.

The origin of side force, at its simplest, is the *Newtonian reaction* to the deflection of fluid particles with greater momentum toward one side of the hull than to the other side due to the hull being aligned asymmetrically to the water flow. Bernoulli's equation, used in HYDRO- and AERODYNAMICS, shows that the static pressure is lower on the side which has the higher water velocity past it. Thus a sail (or hull) is essentially drawn sideways by the leeside static pressure being lower than the mean value due to its higher streaming speed, assisted to a lesser degree by the excess pressure or slower streaming speed on the windward side.

Finally, it should be noted that however small the drag angles can be made for sails and hulls, there will be no point if the opposing aerodynamic and hydrodynamic side forces in practice cause such heeling of the vessel that the side force is seriously reduced. Therefore additional qualities required for windward performance are those associated with *righting stability*: low center of gravity or deep heavy keels, lightweight spars and topsides coupled with high *center of buoyancy*.

Developing designs

The particularly successful sailing vessels of the past can now be assessed in terms of these criteria for good windward performance. There is much evidence to suggest that the ability to hold station with the early square sail was first exhibited by the phenomenal North Atlantic voyages of the Norse longships of the seventh to tenth centuries. These ships, ranging in size from 70 to 270 feet (21 to 82 m) had hulls which even today are considered to have an excellent low drag profile, while the sail rigging exhibited for the first time special cordage (*bowlines*) and spars (*beitass*) so arranged as to tighten the luff and to insure that the sail remains correctly shaped at low angles of wind incidence.

Square sails can also be kept in shape at low incidence by incorporating stiff horizontal battens of bamboo, as in the early Chinese junks, which also had low silhouettes and good underwater charac-

Above: The bridge of the Shin Aitoku Maru, the first completely automatic sail-assisted commercial ship. It is claimed that a crew of eight can operate the ship. The sails are controlled (right) by a computer so they can develop maximum power. The main engine output is also controlled by the computer so that it complements the power developed by the sails efficiently.
Far right: The Shin Aitoku Maru, seen here undergoing sea trials, was launched in 1980 in Japan.

teristics, having developed the more efficient central rudder centuries before European vessels.

Sail in which the yard was used at such an angle to the mast that it acted as a stiff leading edge, the so-called *lateen* (after latin) sail, could be set close to the wind and so contributed much to the technique of windward sailing. Its earliest appearance in the ocean-going Polynesian sailing canoes of the fifth century, and especially in the Mediterranean from the ninth to thirteenth centuries, led to classes of boats whose high efficiency contributed much to the well-documented exploration and merchanting exploits of the Venetians and Portuguese *caravels*, continuing a chain of development which includes the Scandinavian seventeenth-century *jachts* (present word yacht) and the famous Massachusetts *schooners*, which became the direct forerunners of the modern ocean racer. In this development process, it seems probable that the lateen sail was split into two more manageable sails: the foresail whose leading edge was sharpened by replacing the oblique yard by a permanently set sail luff, and the aft or mainsail suspended on the aft portion of the yard which then became the *gaff*. This latter spar eventually disappeared when it became necessary to reduce topside weight and in the process left the modern *Bermudan* sail which exhibited windward advantages now ascribed to its height compared with its length, or *aspect ratio*.

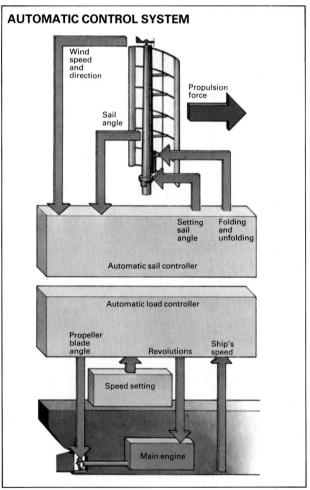

AUTOMATIC CONTROL SYSTEM

Wind speed and direction

Propulsion force

Sail angle

Setting sail angle

Folding and unfolding

Automatic sail controller

Automatic load controller

Propeller blade angle

Revolutions

Ship's speed

Speed setting

Main engine

Modern design

Developments of sailing vessels in this century are based on long experience, together with all the current scientific measuring and deductive techniques. Models of sails and rigging are tested in WIND TUNNELS in the same way as aircraft models are tested, the major measurements being those of drag force, side force and *center of effort* (the point on which the combined effect of the sails and rigging can be said to act) as the speed and angle of incidence of the wind, and also sometimes the heel angle of the sail, are varied. The forces measured on the models by DYNAMOMETERS are then scaled to predict the actual forces to be expected on a full-size rig. Similarly, models of hulls are towed to different speeds and attitudes in towing tanks and the drag force, side force and center of effort (in this case usually called *center of lateral resistance*) acting on the model are measured and scaled to predict the actual forces expected on the full-size hull. Such measurements are most often used as comparisons to check possible advantages of small variations.

It can be recognized, perhaps, that the many measurements required to completely predict an un-

built yacht's performance require the skills and instrumental resources of both aerodynamic and hydrodynamic laboratories and demand more actual measurements than required for an aircraft and ship together. It is not surprising, therefore, that such a full program of measurement is rarely performed for an end product which is essentially recreational. More usually, yacht development arises from a mixture of limited wind tunnel and towing tank tests, together with experience of successful yachts and also trial and error with new boats.

With the heyday of the great sailing ships seemingly gone forever and wind power the province only of sports enthusiasts and weekend sailors, it is interesting to note the development of a new generation of bulk-carrying sailing ships. In Japan, Germany and Britain there are plans, in varying stages of completion, for both windjammer and tanker-style sailing ships that combine new technology and ancient skills. The 12,000 ton displacement, English designed Sailiner is based on the traditional square-rigged windjammer and has auxiliary diesel power.

Sailing boats, as for all other technologies, have always advanced as a result of improvements in materials of construction. Sails need strong, lightweight, fairly stiff, smooth-surfaced, bacteria- and sunshine-resistant fabrics with little mechanical fatigue and which will not let the wind through. Vast improvements in most of these properties have been made by replacing natural fibers by woven and hot calendered (passed through heated rollers) synthetic fibers, particularly Dacron polyester, but there is still room for improvement. Rigging needs materials of high intrinsic tensile strength (strength for weight) and density, while spars need materials of high intrinsic stiffness together with high corrosion resistance. Hemp, then iron, then galvanized steel have been replaced by stainless steel rigging, while anodized aluminum alloy tubes, fiber or honeycomb composites now replace wooden spars. Hulls need corrosion-resistant materials suitable for forming into smooth, lightweight skins of great strength and shock resistance and that most excellent material, wood, is being replaced by aluminum alloys and fiber-reinforced plastics.

See also: Boat building; Sea rescue.

The winter sails

Anders Ansar, a Swedish engineer, astonished his fellow ice sailors one winter's day in 1976. Like everyone else, he strapped the ice sailor's custom-built skates to his boots, but instead of taking hold of the usual skate sail, a cross between a sail and a kite, he wriggled inside something that looked like an upright airplane wing. The *leading edge* was made of transparent plastic, so he could see out, the rest was of sailcloth. Leaning into the wind, he shot away, on one skate, at what appeared to be a remarkable speed, even for an ice craft.

Two basic types of ice craft were used until Ansar's *ice wing* revolutionized the sport. First came the ice boats, with hull, outriggers and mast, carrying large areas of sail. These are the heavy cruisers of the ice sailing fleets. The skate sails, however, are light and maneuverable. Both are hampered by drag – not least from the sailor's body encountering the airstream as it rushes past.

That day in 1976, Ansar, supremely streamlined inside his wing, finished the standard 6 miles (10 km) triangular course 1.2 miles (2 km) ahead of the nearest skate sail. In later tests, he showed he could do 47 mph (75 km/h) in a 22 mph (35 km/h) breeze, and in really stiff winds, 62 mph (100 km/h) – a great deal faster than the traditional craft, which achieve 30 mph (50 km/h) on average days, and 50 mph (80 km/h) in stiff breezes. The new device was promptly consigned to a class of its own, and the skate sailors (until then a no-rules class, allowing freedom of design for each and every craft) quickly introduced a set of regulations to protect them from further outlandish inventions.

The remarkable performance of the ice wing boils down to aerodynamics, and the aerodynamics of sailing are similar to those of flying. Central to them is the fact that air behaves like a fluid. It flows; when separated it likes to rejoin itself. And it is viscous – sticky – so that when it meets a surface, it attaches to it, even if the surface is curved and requires a change in the direction of flow.

Air meeting the rounded leading edge of an airplane wing behaves just like this. The particles deflected over the curved upper surface attach themselves to it; those going beneath carry straight on – because the underside is generally straight. To make good the extra distance traveled, the air particles flowing over the upper wing surface have to speed up. This results in a drop in pressure over the upper surface. A drop in pressure amounts to a partial vacuum, which the wing tries to fill by lifting.

Much the same occurs with a sail on a boat to produce driving power, except when the boat goes downwind, when it is simply pushed along. To go across the wind, or make good up to the wind,

Below left: The traditional ice boat appears clumsy in comparison with Anders Ansar's sleek ice wing (below right). The ice wing's design minimizes drag, so the craft can do up to 62 mph, compared with the ice boat's 50 mph.

Above: Skates for use with the ice wing have to be specially made; they are worn with ski boots to give the ankles support at high speeds.
Right: The ice wing is symmetrical, so the craft can sail equally well on different tacks, particularly at speed.

boats rely on the aerodynamic properties of sails, rather than hull design. Like wings, they have rounded leading edges, and they flatten out toward the back. Wind blowing into the windward side of the sail inflates it to produce the shape which is specially tailored into it by the sailmaker. Air flowing round the other, downwind side (properly called the lee side of the sail) attaches itself to the curvature and causes a drop in pressure (just as on a wing), and this in turn creates a suction force in a generally leeward direction.

The boat heels, and only the keel sticking down into the water prevents it from capsizing (together with what the crew, in a dinghy, can contribute by leaning out). This (together with certain aspects of hull design) translates the forces acting to leeward into a forward movement. These are not the only principles which operate to produce sail power, but they are the most important, and they also apply to ice craft. Instead of a center plate, ice boats use outriggers with runners. A runner sliding over ice encounters less friction than a hull sliding through water, hence the superior speed of ice craft.

The ice wing does even better. Its leading edge develops aerodynamic forces which are much stronger than those created by the somewhat clumsy profile of the conventional mast and sail. It is smooth and creates comparatively little drag. Nor is there any drag from the airstream meeting the sailor's body, the hull, outriggers or other solid parts. The sail area is smaller, too, so there is less drag on the sail itself. The ice wing runs on only one skate, which causes less friction. In addition, the wing has certain characteristics which are all its own, and which contribute to the performance. The most obvious is the fact that the wing is symmetric – curved similarly on both sides – and can sail equally well on different tacks with the wind blowing onto one side or the other.

The leading edge of the wing is made of transparent plastic shaped by internally mounted ribs. The remainder is sailcloth, stretched on internal rigging of aluminum tubing. Inside, the sailor supports the structure by means of a pair of shoulder straps, and holds onto a small bar in front of him or her. Facing forward, the sailor not only has adequate vision through the transparent leading edge but also protection from the cold wind.

Salt, chemical

A chemical compound formed when the hydrogen of an acid is replaced by a metal, or a group of atoms which is electropositive such as an ammonium ION, NH_4^+, is known as a *salt*. Salts are named after the parent acid, so sulfates are derived from sulfuric acid, chlorides from hydrochloric acid, nitrates from nitric acid and so on. Common salt, sodium chloride (NaCl), is by far the most abundant naturally occurring salt; there are many thousands of millions of tons of it in the oceans alone. It can be prepared by neutralizing sodium hydroxide (NaOH) with hydrochloric acid (HCl):

$$NaOH + HCl \rightarrow NaCl + H_2O$$

NaOH	+ HCl	→ NaCl	+ H_2O
sodium hydroxide	hydrochloric acid	sodium chloride	water

Right: The red liquid, a solution of cobalt chloride ($CoCl_2$) in water, is cooled to produce crystals of the salt. In the background another salt, sodium hydrogen selenite ($NaHSeO_3$) is being dried.
Below: By replacing hydrogen in phosphoric acid with ammonia, this plant manufactures ammonium phosphate to be used in the production of yeast, flame-retardant materials and horticultural fertilizers.

Apart from the commonest method, that is, neutralizing an acid with an alkali, salts can be formed by dissolving a metal in acid, for example zinc in sulfuric acid to produce sulfate, or reacting a metal carbonate with acid, so sodium carbonate reacted with hydrochloric acid results in sodium chloride, and also carbon dioxide and water. Other methods are more specific. For example ammonium salts may be formed by passing ammonia gas through a dilute solution of the appropriate acid. Not all salts are soluble in water: if solutions of sodium chloride and silver nitrate are mixed, insoluble silver chloride precipitates out of the solution.

Salts are *ionic* compounds composed of *cations*, which are positively charged, and *anions*, which are negatively charged. In the solid state, salts are crystalline, and the ions are distributed regularly throughout the crystal lattice. Sodium chloride, for example, has a cubic crystal structure with each sodium ion (Na^+) being surrounded by six chloride ions (Cl^-) and vice versa. Many salts can be dissolved in water, and the resulting solutions may be regarded as intimate mixtures of water molecules and the anions and cations composing the salt. Whether it is dissolved or not, a salt must remain electrically neutral, and this means that the component anions and cations must be present in a fixed ratio. In copper chloride, for example, each copper ion (Cu^{++}) has a double positive charge and each chloride ion (Cl^-) has a single negative charge, so that in order to remain electrically neutral there must be twice as many chloride ions as copper ions.

Types of salt

Salts can be broadly divided into three categories: *simple salts*, *double salts* and *complex salts*. Simple salts contain a single metal ion and examples include sodium chloride, $NaCl$, sodium bicarbonate, $NaHCO_3$, sodium carbonate (washing soda), Na_2CO_3, copper sulfate, $CuSO_4$, and potassium nitrate, KNO_3, a constituent of gunpowder.

Double salts are salts containing at least two types of metal ion, and among the most important are the *alums* which are sulfates containing chromium ions, Cr^{+++}, or aluminum ions, Al^{+++}, and an ALKALI METAL ion, usually sodium, Na^+, or potassium, K^+. From a commercial point of view the most important alum is potassium aluminum sulfate, $KAl(SO_4)_2.12H_2O$, called *potash alum*, which acts as a mordant in DYEING processes, in other words it helps bind the dye to the fabric being dyed. Water molecules are an integral part of the crystalline structure of alums and they are usually represented in the chemical formula.

Complex salts are salts in which one of the ions comprises a metal atom bound to one or more other chemical groups. Such an ion is called a *complex ion* and it remains as a separate entity when the salt is dissolved. *Potassium ferricyanide*, $K_3Fe(CN)_6$, used as a fertilizer and in some dyeing processes, is a complex salt composed of potassium ions, K^+, and ferricyanide ions, $Fe(CN)_6^{---}$; and *cuprammonium chloride*, $Cu(NH_3)_4Cl_2$, which, in aqueous solution, is capable of dissolving cellulose, contains the complex ion $Cu(NH_3)_4^{++}$ and chloride ions (Cl^-).

Not all salts are completely neutral when they are dissolved in water; some will be found to be slightly alkaline and have a pH greater than 7, while some will be slightly acid and have a pH less than 7. The reason for this is usually a reversible reaction between one or other of the ions in the salt and water molecules to produce either alkaline hydroxyl ions (OH^-) or acid hydrogen ions (H^+). Sodium acetate, CH_3COONa, for example, is slightly alkaline in solution whereas ammonium chloride (NH_4Cl) is slightly acid:

CH_3COO^-	+	H_2O	$\rightleftharpoons$	CH_3COOH	+	OH^-
acetate ion		water		hydrogen acetate		hydroxyl ion

NH_4	+	H_2O	$\rightleftharpoons$	NH_4OH	+	H^+
ammonium ion		water		ammonium hydroxide		hydrogen ion

See also: Atom and molecule; Salt production.

Below: The Minerva hot springs in Yellowstone National Park, Wyoming, flow over natural steps, leaving white mineral deposits on the rock.

Salt production

Common salt, sodium chloride (NaCl), is widely distributed throughout the Earth's crust; every gallon (4.5 liters) of sea water contains about 4 oz (113 g) of it. Huge deposits of rock salt, or *halite*, formed by the evaporation of sea water in geological periods exist in many parts of the world, notably in the U.S., Canada and Mexico, the U.S.S.R. and Europe. In the U.S. major salt deposits are exploited in Michigan, New York, Ohio, Louisiana and Kansas, with additional workings in other areas.

Mining

Rock salt deposits are worked by well-used mining techniques and if the salt is sufficiently pure, as in certain parts of the U.S., it can be used without further purification. Mining is usually done by the room and pillar method which insures that substantial rock salt pillars are left for support.

In a typical salt mine the working height is approximately 25 ft (7.6 m) with the working faces being around 50 ft (15 m) wide according to the local conditions. The face is undercut to a depth of 12 ft (3.7 m), using a heavy-duty rock-cutting machine, and then drilled to a standard pattern with a mobile hydraulic rotary drilling carriage. The face is then charged with explosives and short-delay detonators. Firing the explosives produces a heap of over 1000 tons of well-fragmented rock salt ready for loading. The rock salt is transported from the face by 24-ton diesel dumpers to the head of a conveyer belt system which carries it to an underground crushing plant. From the crusher a further system of conveyer belts

takes the processed rock salt to the base of the mineshaft, where it is hoisted to the surface.

When mined, the purity of rock salt is generally greater than 97 per cent and for many uses only requires crushing and grading. If pure salt is required the mined material may be dissolved in water to form brine which is then evaporated by one of the methods described below. Alternatively the salt may be extracted directly by drilling boreholes down into the salt deposits. Water is then pumped down the boreholes to dissolve the salt, forming brine which is pumped back up to the surface for evaporation. This leaves insoluble impurities behind, which are needed with this technique to avoid subsidence of the overlying land as the salt layer is dissolved away.

Open-pan evaporation

This was one of the earliest and most common methods of extracting salt from brine, though for many applications it has been replaced by the vacuum method. The brine is evaporated in long, shallow pans up to 150 ft (45 m) long by 10 ft (3 m), or more. Heat is supplied by steam pipes near the bottom of the pan or directly to the bottom using hot gases from a fire. Salt crystals formed in the brine fall to the bottom of the pan where they are removed by a scraper system. The salt produced by this process is in the form of characteristic flaky crystals and is known as *flake* or *grainer* salt.

Solar evaporation

Salt is produced from seawater by this method in many countries, including the U.S., the U.S.S.R., India, France, Spain, Italy and Israel. The process

Left: In a salt mine, rock dislodged by blasting is shifted by large mechanical shovels. The salt is carried from the face to an underground crushing plant, the product of which is transported by conveyer belts to the surface. Salts, such as common salt and potassium carbonate are mined by the room-and-pillar method, by which columns of mineral are left to support the roof.

simply uses the heat from the Sun to evaporate brine in open ponds. The brine is usually run first into large *concentration ponds* with a surface area of up to about 50 acres (20 hectares) where impurities such as clay and sand, and the less soluble salts such as calcium carbonate and calcium sulfate, separate out. The concentrated brine is then run through a series of smaller *crystallizing pans* where salt of varying grades is deposited. The best-grade salt is obtained in the first crystallizing pan.

Vacuum evaporation

A typical vacuum plant for salt making consists of a series of three or more closed vertical cylindrical vessels with conical bottoms. Each of these vessels, or *effects* as they are generally called, has a steam chamber or *calandria* either totally submerged in the brine to be evaporated or externally connected. The calandrias contain a large number of vertical tubes through which the brine can be circulated, an arrangement which exposes a very large surface area. This system is most efficient for transferring the heat of the steam to the brine.

The first vessel receives steam into its calandria from an outside source (often exhaust steam from the turbines of electricity generators) and the brine in the first vessel begins to boil. The steam in the calandria, having given up much of its heat to the brine, is condensed into water and drained off. The boiling brine, however, is now generating its own steam which is piped over the calandria in the second vessel of the series and transfers its heat to more brine. In the same way steam from the boiling brine in the second vessel is used in turn to heat brine in the third vessel, and so on. The steam released from the brine in the last vessel of the series is condensed by cold water.

The condensation of the steam from the boiling brine in each vessel produces a reduction in pressure, and because of this the brine boils at temperatures lower than would be the case at ordinary atmospheric pressures. Pressures, and hence boiling temperatures, become successively lower throughout the series, and in the last vessel the pressure is approaching a vacuum and the brine boils at little more than blood temperature. The salt crystals which form are taken from the bottom of the vessels and pumped in the form of a slurry to filters which separate the salt crystals from the brine. The salt is then taken by conveyer belt either to a warehouse as undried *vacuum salt*, or passed through driers to produce dried vacuum salt which is stored in silos. *Granular salt* is produced in a multiple-effect evaporator of specialized design in which the salt crystals are prevented from leaving the body of the boiling brine before they have had time to grow to the required size. In the manufacture of *dendritic salt* the crystals are induced to

Above: Salt production in the Canary Islands. Concentrated brine is run into crystallizing pans where various grades of salt are deposited.

change their shape from the usual cubic form and develop branches, giving a small spiky crystal with a relatively large surface area.

Uses

More than 60 per cent of the salt produced is used in the chemical industry for the manufacture of basic industrial chemicals such as chlorine, sodium hydroxide (caustic soda), and hydrochloric acid. Another significant use is in the food industry – in the U.S. consumption of salt is more than one million tons a year. Table salt usually has a small quantity of an anti-caking agent such as sodium carbonate added to insure that it flows freely. Other uses of salt include highway deicing, and the regeneration of ion exchange resins in water softeners.

See also: Salt, chemical; Mining techniques.

Salvage, marine

Marine salvage is the recovery of objects lost or damaged in the oceans, and the salvaging techniques may apply also to lakes and rivers. In modern times many objects ranging from treasure to hydrogen bombs, as well as wrecked ships, have been recovered by salvage operations.

Towing

If a ship is disabled, for example because of failure of the main engines or the steering gear, or damaged by a collision so that it is unable to proceed under its own power, it can be towed to a port or sheltered location by a salvage tug. These tugs are specifically designed for towing with strong cable attachment points. Tugs intended for deep sea salvage may be more than 250 ft (76 m) long with engine ratings of more than 15,000 hp (11,250 kW) to give a pulling effort of more than 100 tons.

Grounded ships

A ship which has run aground may seem, at first, to be a simple salvage job, but each salvage operation is different, and ingenuity is always important. If a ship has simply run aground, it may be necessary only to wait for the next high tide and pull it afloat again, but this depends upon the circumstances. If a ship goes aground in a rocky, treacherous terrain, its hull may be broken when the tide goes out. If the hull suffers some damage from running aground, it may be possible to make temporary repairs, with steel or wooden patches, which the water pressure will help to hold in place when the ship is afloat.

If a vessel has been driven high aground by winds and waves, it may still be possible to refloat it by *lightening ship*. Freight, fixtures and even the ship's superstructure may be removed and transferred to waiting barges, but it is important to anchor the ship in the direction of deep water before lightening begins, so that in its lightened condition it does not go further aground.

Sunken ships

Whether sunken ships can be salvaged depends upon a combination of factors: depth of water, size of the ship, weather conditions, availability of equipment, estimated cost, and so on. The larger the ship to be salvaged the more difficult the job will be at a given depth, because the amount of lift available from the different types of equipment used is limited.

If the ship has sunk in shallow water so that the main deck is out of water it can usually be refloated by patching any holes and pumping the water out. When the ship is completely underwater, however, more elaborate techniques have to be used, and

Above: A diver examining a beam of The Mary Rose, which sunk during the sixteenth century.

effective salvage operations became possible only during the past 100 years with the development of suitable technology.

Often the location of the vessel to be salvaged is known from the records of the sinking, but abandoned vessels may eventually sink some distance from where they were left. With aircraft (which often have to be recovered to establish the causes of a crash) precise location may be more difficult. Accordingly, the first operation is usually to find the wreck. If the wreck lies in shallow water it may be possible to see it from the air, and in deeper water SONAR is used. Sonar (SOund NAvigation Ranging) operates on the principle that sound travels through a medium at constant, measurable velocity; thus the time it takes for a sound signal to reflect from an underwater object can be translated into a measurement of distance. Computer processing of the sonar signals allows a picture of the sea bed to be built up with unexpected shapes possibly indicating the presence of a wreck. Problems can occur, though, if a vessel or aircraft has sunk in an area where the

ocean floor is naturally rough, because it will be difficult to distinguish between natural and unnatural projections.

Once the wreck is located, the work of the divers begins. Mechanical lifting by floating cranes is still the most popular method, as it has been since the invention of the diving suit made it possible to attach cables and chains to the hulk. The laying of cables is done so that the sunken vessel is cradled by supporting gear which leads to the surface; the cables are frequently positioned by dredgers, with the assistance of divers, and the chief considerations are the size of the hulk, the power and buoyancy of the surface vessels and the unpredictability of the weather. If the cables are improperly positioned or if the weight of the hulk shifts as it is being lifted, weeks of work may be wasted, the stricken vessel may break its back or slip out of the matrix of cable and go back to the bottom.

A sunken vessel is likely to be mired in mud at the bottom, and the effect is a powerful force of static friction or suction. The force required to break the suction will be many times the force required to lift the vessel once it is free, with the result of a sudden increase in the rate of the vessel's motion. This can break the ship's hull or at least cause it to be difficult to control. Ingenious methods have been devised to deal with this problem. Cables from the positive and negative terminals on a generator on the surface vessel can be directed to two sides of a sunken hull so that they become positive and negative electrodes. When the power is turned on, the

Above: Raising the final starboard section of the hull of The Mary Rose on October 11, 1982. The hull, supported by a steel cradle, is suspended beneath a lifting frame. The salvage of The Mary Rose was particularly difficult because the vessel was extremely delicate and likely to break up when disturbed. Even a modern, steel-hulled vessel is likely to break up if it is lifted.
Right: The hull of The Mary Rose breaking the surface of the water.

Left: A World War II Wellington bomber which crashed into Loch Ness, Scotland, is recovered, using land-based lifting gear.

cubic foot of this foam weighs 2 lb (0.907 kg) and displaces 64 lb (29 kg) of water. Polyurethane beads or pressure-injected spheres are even better, because they are easier to remove from the recovered hull than solid foam. These are pumped into the hull through a pipe. The pressure-injected spheres are 11 in. (279 mm) in diameter, providing 30 lb (13.6 kg) of buoyancy; they are pressurized to synchronize with ambient pressure at a given depth and are equipped with valves which allow internal pressure to adjust as necessary when the ship rises.

The *prop wash* is an elbow-shaped aluminum tube which fits on the transom of a boat. The wash from the ship's propeller is directed through it to the sand at the bottom, so that digging operations which used to take days for divers can sometimes be accomplished in a few minutes. Pumps are also used to provide the necessary water flow. The *air lift* is used to recover small objects. It is an open-ended pipe; a hose from the surface supplies compressed air to a perforated chamber at the lower end of the pipe. The air bubbles rush upward, creating suction which carries small objects with it.

water between the electrodes acts as a conductor; ELECTROLYSIS results, and the water is broken up into hydrogen and oxygen; hydrogen bubbles attach themselves to the hull, displacing the mud and destroying the static friction.

Other lifting methods
Mechanical lifts are often aided by other devices, such as *pontoons*. These are empty metal tanks or rubber bags which are flooded, sunk, arranged around the hulk, and finally pumped free of water with compressed air, buoyancy resulting. Pontoons were developed especially for rescuing submarines.

Compressed air is often used without pontoons. Apertures and leaks are sealed by divers so that the vessel becomes relatively airtight; most seagoing vessels have been constructed in compartment form anyway, so it is often not necessary to seal up the whole of a wreck before pumping in compressed air.

Mechanical lifting can be aided by the tides as well. Partially flooded vessels are attached to the sunken hull at low tide, and pumped free of water as the tide rises, providing extra lift. This method is particularly successful where the lifting equipment is insufficiently powerful for the job on hand.

Polyurethane foam has been used to raise vessels. Polyurethane components are sent down in a hose to a mixing chamber that divers have installed near the wreck. Another agent which has a low boiling point is also sent to the chamber, and the materials are mixed and expelled with pressurized nitrogen. The low-boiling agent volatilizes because of the sudden decrease in pressure, and a froth of polyurethane bubbles is produced inside the hull. The bubbles *cure* to form a rigid, cellular material; each

Submersibles
Increasing use is being made of both piloted and remote-controlled submersibles for salvage in deep water. These craft are operated from a mother ship and the most advanced designs are capable of working at depths greater than 15,000 ft (4570 m) though most have a more restricted working depth of around 6000 ft (1830 m). External manipulator systems allow objects to be recovered or worked on and cables attached for lifting, though the lifting capacity is generally limited. Sonar systems and MAGNETOMETERS are fitted to allow examination and searches of the sea bed, along with lighting systems and cameras. Remote-controlled units are connected to the mother ship by control and power cables (which are also used for some piloted units) and have low-light television cameras to allow the operator to view the working area.

Destroying wrecks
Salvage companies are often asked to destroy or remove a wreck rather than to recover it; during wartime scuttled or sunken ships often blocked ports, for example. Sometimes the wreck is recovered and towed to deeper water to be sunk again, but explosives are also used. A ring of explosives is placed around the wreck and detonated; tons of water suddenly converge on the hulk, crushing it.

See also: Electrolysis; Ship; Steering gear.

Sand and shot blasting

In many manufacturing processes there is a need to clean and smooth components at some stage during manufacture, and various forms of blasting techniques have been developed to do this. The different techniques used are commonly referred to as sand and shot blasting, although sand is no longer used as an abrasive. Generally, a stream of abrasive particles is directed over and against the part at high speed so that the abrasive impact cleans the surface thoroughly.

Typical applications include the removal of sand cores and scale from castings prior to machining, surface preparation for painting, cleaning of used components for servicing or refurbishing, and the *deflashing* of plastics moldings.

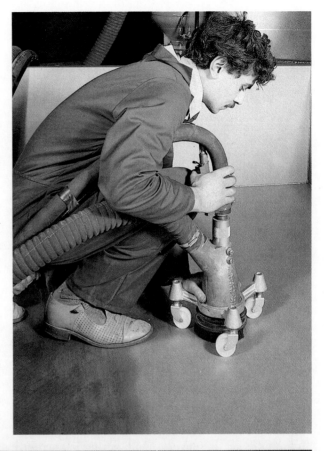

Machine types

A number of methods are used to produce the stream of abrasive particles, the most usual being to use a blast of compressed air. The abrasive is fed into a rapidly moving stream of compressed air and carried to the workpiece. The abrasive blast may be directed over the workpiece manually or in a predetermined cycle, and generally blasting is carried out in an enclosed blast room or cabinet. Blast rooms are used for large components; the operator

Above right: A castored blasting gun used to clean a large, welded steel box. Dust and debris are carried by a vacuum recovery tube to a reclaimer section. Here an adjustable air-wash and sieving system are used to cleanse the recycled blasting medium to insure its quality is maintained.
Right: An aircraft undercarriage component is blasted clean.

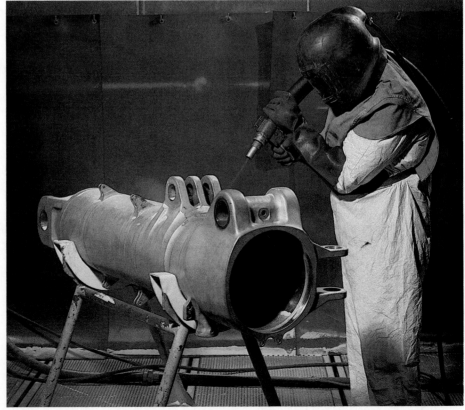

Left: The blast cleaning of structural steel has several advantages: it reduces contamination of the workshop floor, it increases the life of drills and punching tools, and it makes marking out and preparation work easier. Most important, it produces an ideal surface for subsequent coatings, and the result is a finer finish and better quality.

works within the room, protected by appropriate clothing, ear protectors, and masks.

In closed circuit blast systems the blast nozzle is surrounded by a recovery head, which is normally sealed to the work surface by a flexible brush arrangement. Abrasive from the blast nozzle strikes the work surface and is retained in the working area by the recovery unit; a suction system takes the abrasive from the work area back to a reclaimer unit. Here, the abrasive is cleaned before being fed back to a hopper ready for reuse.

The abrasive effect varies with the medium used and the pressure of the blast air. For cleaning and descaling iron and steel parts pressures in the range of 50 to 100 lb/sq in. (3.44 to 6.89 bar) are normally used, with lower pressures of 10 to 60 lb/sq in. (0.68 to 4.13 bar) being used for the softer nonferrous metals. Typical nozzle sizes are 0.25 to 0.4 in. (6 to 10 mm) diameter with air flows of up to 100 cu ft (3 cu m) being used with the larger nozzles and high working-pressures. Wear-resistant materials such as tungsten and boron carbide are used for the nozzles. The necessary air flow may also be produced by suction in closed-circuit systems; it has a softer action and is particularly suitable for surface finishing applications. After blasting, abrasive particles and dust on the work surface are cleaned off with an air blast.

In another design of machine, the abrasive is carried in a water stream to give *wet blasting*. The use of water to carry the abrasive allows high flow rates, with up to 30 per cent of the flow being abrasive particles. The abrasive slurry is recirculated by a special pump system that also agitates it during operation to insure good mixing of the abrasive and water. The wet-blasting process is dust free.

Mechanical methods are also used to provide a stream of abrasive for blasting applications. Abrasive is fed into the center of a rapidly rotating wheel with radial guide vanes, and centrifugal action throws the abrasive out in a fast-moving stream that is directed onto the workpiece. The spent abrasive falls to the bottom of the blast chamber where it is recovered and fed to a *separator*. Here, the abrasive is cleaned before being fed back to the IMPELLER wheels.

Abrasives

A wide range of abrasive media are available to suit different cleaning and finishing applications. Silica sand, while inexpensive, generates toxic dust which gives rise to a risk of the lung disease, silicosis, and its use is now banned in many countries. Other abrasives offer faster action and better control of the process. Iron and steel grit are used for rust and scale removal and for deburring, while alumina abrasives offer fast cutting for surface cleaning. Steel shot gives a fine surface finish and is used for surface *peening*; glass beads have a similar but more gentle action. Plastic parts are deflashed with soft blast abrasives such as nylon and crushed fruit stones, which are also used for fine cleaning and paint removal.

See also: Air; Metal; Protective clothing.

Satellite

Since the Earth's first artificial satellite, Sputnik 1, was launched by the U.S.S.R. in 1957, several hundreds of satellites of increasing size and complexity have been put into orbit, mostly around the Earth. Craft have been orbited around the Sun, Moon and Mars, but these are generally known as space probes.

The use of Earth satellites has many practical benefits to humankind. The world's meteorological services depend increasingly on satellite photographs of cloud cover and on measurements of atmospheric properties made from space. Communications satellites are of great importance, not just for relaying live pictures of sporting events but mainly for providing telephone and data links for governments and industries. The data gathered by scientific satellites have greatly increased our knowledge of the world and its surrounding environment. Major powers use satellites to gather military intelligence.

A satellite must reach a velocity of 25,000 mph (41,000 km/h) to escape from the Earth's gravitational pull, and continue at 18,000 mph (30,000 km/h) to stay in a low orbit. Before the Challenger tragedy the U.S. launched satellites as part of its Space Shuttle program, while the U.S.S.R. and Europe use unmanned *staged* rockets. In the U.S. and Europe satellites are an important commercial concern. In Asia, Japan is taking its first steps into communication satellites. China is also taking the first steps in its satellite program, a sign of the country's increasing importance worldwide.

Working environment

Satellites have to operate in a harsh environment which cannot totally be simulated in ground tests. Equipment must work in zero gravity, under high vacuum conditions and with wide temperature variations. During launch, the vibrations transmitted from the launch vehicle and shock loadings as the upper stages take over are severe. To add to the problems, some materials can emit gas or give off particles of their substance under a vacuum, and have to be avoided, as the particles could confuse star sensors or contaminate solar arrays. Two similar metal surfaces may weld together under pressure in a vacuum, and conventional lubrication systems would not work as the oil would evaporate. Surfaces which have to touch each other are made of dissimilar materials, and solid-film lubrication systems using lead or PTFE (Teflon) are needed.

Construction

The design of a satellite involves a number of subsystems: structure, thermal control, attitude con-

Above: The Spacenet 1 civil telecommunications satellite was launched aboard the French Ariane V9 rocket from French Guyana in May 1984.

trol, power, electricity distribution, telemetry and command, and an operational payload. The payload may be a number of scientific instruments, or cameras to photograph the terrain below.

So that the satellite can carry the maximum payload, its construction must be as light as possible, yet it must maintain its integrity under the strains of launch. Aluminum alloy and conventional aerospace building techniques are generally employed. Floor panels, side walls and solar array frameworks are made from aluminum or glass-fiber laminate-faced honeycomb panels. Threaded inserts fitted to the honeycomb are used to mount the equipment. Machined parts are made from aluminum alloy,

Left: A hurricane photographed from a high-flying piloted aircraft. The picture is of a high quality, but satellites offer several advantages over aircraft for weather observation purposes: they can maintain a constant watch, and over a larger area, whereas an aircraft can only photograph a limited area over a short time. Below: From space, the NOAA 9 satellite was able to chart Hurricane Gloria's progress up the eastern seaboard.

titanium or beryllium – materials chosen for their nonmagnetic properties as well as for their strength and thermal stability. The satellite has to stay correctly balanced under all configurations and conditions; and any spin-stabilized satellite must be designed to be stable in one axis only.

Electronic equipment is sensitive and usually operates within the spacecraft at a temperature of approximately 77° F (25° C). Variations will be just a few degrees from this. The satellite's environment, however, can vary from full sunlight to full eclipse, and it may or may not be illuminated by light reflected from the Earth; surface temperatures on the satellite body exterior can be as high as 320° F (160° C) and as low as −220° F (−140° C). The apparatus on board can vary in its heat output as well, and yet the interior of the satellite must be kept in thermal balance. If the experiments are not too demanding a *passive* control system may be used: the exterior finish of the satellite is chosen to absorb or emit radiation and no further temperature control is needed. For example, a light or shiny finish will neither absorb nor emit very much radiation, whereas a black finish will. Thermal blankets of crinkled multilayer aluminized plastic film are used to insulate some areas.

For complex satellites, an *active* thermal control system is used. A louver system on the spacecraft wall can control the inside temperature, or alternatively heat pipes may carry excess heat away from localized hot spots to the wall of the satellite.

Attitude control

Satellites usually have to be pointed in space in some way so that the solar arrays are always pointing at the Sun. Simple satellites are *spin stabilized* like a GYROSCOPE about one axis, while others are

oriented by a system of control jets fixed to the body – *three-axis stabilization*. With this system, the satellite's orientation has to be measured, so that corrections can be made, and this is carried out by sensors which are designed to observe the position of astronomical bodies such as the Sun, Earth and certain stars. The attitude control system receives this information or an overriding ground command and demands pulses from the control jets to realign it as required. These control jets used to use hydrazine as a fuel – a single propellant which does not have to be mixed with anything else, but which decomposes on contact with a catalyst, but most modern satellites under construction use a bi-propellant system using nitrogen tetroxide and monomethylhydrazine as the fuel. Future satellites may

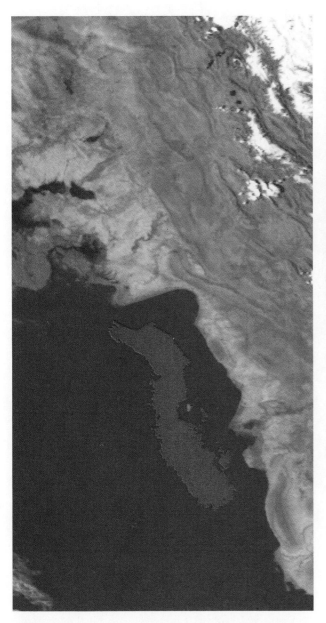

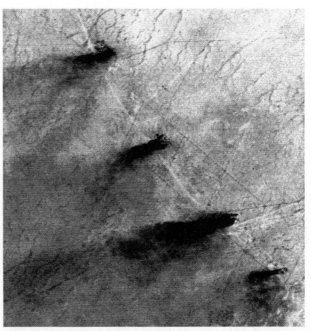

Above: Huge plumes of smoke from gas flares bubble up into the skies above Iraq. The picture was taken using Landsat's Mulitspectral Scanner, which senses in four spectral bands, including infrared, and can see details as small as 260 ft across.

Above: Using its Advanced Very High Resolution Radiometer (AVHRR), the NOAA 7 satellite was able to provide this evidence of an oil spill in the Persian Gulf to environmental protection groups, so they could quickly take action to deal with it.

use ION PROPULSION for the same purpose. Using these systems, a satellite can be pointed with high accuracy – an orbiting craft can be pointed at a selected spot on the ground below to an accuracy of 33 ft (10 m), for example.

Electric power

Satellites in Earth orbit have almost unlimited supplies of power available from the Sun. Solar cells are either mounted around the body or are on panels

• FACT FILE •

- Solar Max, a satellite launched in 1980 to monitor solar flares, had to be repaired in orbit by the crew of the Challenger Space Shuttle after blowing fuses ten months into its mission. Using a backpack propulsion unit astronaut George Nelson stabilized the satellite's wobble so that it could be captured, repaired, and relaunched.

- The LEASAT series of geostationary satellites used by the U.S. Navy, orbiting at an altitude of 22,300 miles (35,900 km) above the Earth, were the first satellites specifically designed for shuttle launch. With a diameter of 14 ft (4.2 m), they are too large for any other launching vehicle.

- The first satellite salvaging operation took place in November 1984 when the Palapa B–2 satellite was coaxed into Challenger's cargo hold by spacewalking astronauts. Two days later a second satellite, Westar 6, was also rescued. Both had been launched unsuccessfully the previous February.

Above: Astronauts Dale Gardner and Joe Allen capture the defunct Westar VI communications satellite, photographed from the Space Shuttle. Westar's boosters had earlier failed to fire, so it never achieved geostationary orbit.

which can be extended from the sides of the satellite on light spars. Since there is no air in space, and since the satellite is weightless with hardly any strain imposed on it, these panels can be very lightly constructed. A panel of 21.5 sq ft (2 sq m), the size of a tabletop, can generally provide 500 watts of power all the time it is in sunlight. A battery provides power for emergencies and for when the craft is in the Earth's shadow.

Satellites have a limited lifetime for a number of reasons. The output of the solar cells decreases with time, a fact which can be allowed for by producing excess power to start with which is reradiated as heat into space from special panels. The attitude control systems have only a certain amount of fuel; and the satellite itself may encounter sufficient air resistance to bring the craft out of orbit to burn up in the atmosphere in a comparatively short time.

Lifetimes of two to ten years are common, but as space travel becomes more commonplace, maintenance programs will become possible.

Applications

Communications satellites are an important part of the information revolution. Telephone calls, computer data, TV and still pictures can be transmitted across the world via satellite. Cheaper global communications are becoming available as each new satellite is launched.

Weather satellites are in constant use providing pictures of cloud cover over the Earth. By observing infrared wavelengths, they can operate at night, since there is a temperature difference between cloudy and clear areas. One system transmits pictures continuously so that anyone with a suitable receiver on the ground can pick up signals and convert them on a facsimile machine to a photograph of the region as seen from space. Other satellites have been proposed which will carry out tasks more economically than ground systems – for example, to help oceanographers construct accurate profiles of currents, temperatures and densities of the oceans,

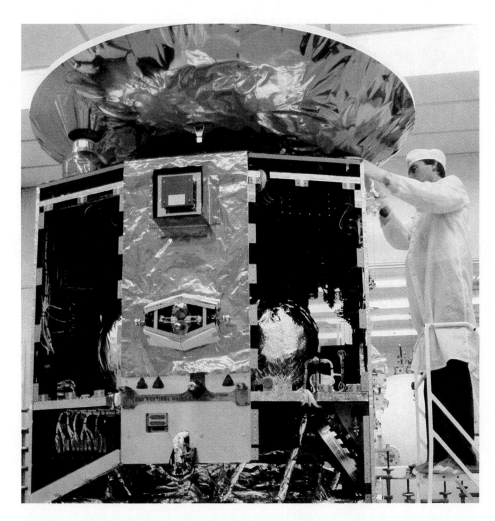

Left: The Marecs B2 satellite in its final stages of construction. The Marecs series of satellites were constructed by a consortium of European aerospace companies for the International Maritime Organisation, Inmarsat. Launched in 1984, Marecs B2 operates in conjunction with the other Inmarsat Marecs satellites to provide a global telecommunications service between ships at sea and shore establishments.

a task which would be almost impossible by conventional means. Such information, together with satellite data on the polar caps, is of great value not only to the meteorologist and hydrologist but also to such people as deep-sea fishermen.

The Earth's resources can be studied from space far more effectively than from ground level. By using cameras which take images in several different color bands, potential diseased crop areas can be spotted as a result of the effect on the reflectivity of the plants. Mineral resources, cattle grazing densities, forestry and water supplies can all be surveyed rapidly from space. An experimental satellite, the Earth Resources Technology Satellite, has proved remarkably successful in this respect: its images show ground features as small as 300 ft (90 m) from an altitude of 570 miles (914 km). Such a satellite can also detect pollution sources: oil tankers are now under surveillance and can no longer risk prosecution for illegal tank washing and dumping oil at sea.

New roles for satellites seem assured in the future – commercial, scientific and military. Some scientists envisage manufacturing in space, although a plan to manufacture biomaterials there has recently been postponed by the drug company involved. Astronomers are planning large satellite-based telescopes; these will be able to observe the heavens in far more detail than ever before.

Despite the ever-increasing importance of commercial satellites, the military still provide most of the cash and impetus behind satellite programs. The traditional role of satellites where high-quality pictures are relayed back to Earth to be analyzed seems to be about to be supplanted by a new role. President Reagan's Strategic Defense Initiative (SDI), or Star Wars, is still in its infancy, but billions of dollars have been promised to scientists who can develop this nuclear defense system. Highly sophisticated computer-controlled laser satellites are being planned which could destroy incoming missiles. Some scientists have great reservations about whether SDI can ever work properly, but the funding given to scientists working in the satellite field can only make these devices more commonplace.

See also: Communications satellite; Space photography; Space probe; Space shuttle.

Trail of an eye in the sky

Four hundred miles above the Earth the watcher is at work. An object roughly the size of a large automobile spinning the globe 14 times a day. Sensitive enough to take pictures the size of a tennis court far below – and to do so through fog, cloud, and pitch darkness. The object is Landsat – maybe the most remarkable machine ever built. Maybe the best friend in space to guide the planet's future.

Landsat's eye is not open to the colors we see, but to the long wavelengths of infrared and the short wavelengths of radio. Everything warmed by the Sun or fueled by Earth's inner chemistry produces a reflected message that Landsat can gather at a glance. The instruments on board pick up the different infrared signals and interpret them whether they are from vegetation, rock, soil, water or animals. The images are digitized and transmitted to Earth-based receiving stations where they are converted to color or black-and-white pictures of amazing meaning.

Following Landsat (or Seasat, its companion) on a typical day's work, the satellite makes a north–south circular orbit and as the Earth rotates westward beneath it so the coverage of land and ocean shifts. Every 18 days, having completed 252 orbits, a single satellite can report on nearly every point on the Earth. So on this day, 14 orbits, an appropriately equipped satellite could be involved in the following types of mission.

Orbit 1. Agricultural survey. A sweep of Imperial Valley, California, revealed 25 separate crops in 8865 fields. The satellite detected the onset of a disease in some of the crops before it was apparent to the farmer on the ground.

Orbit 2. Location of mineral deposits by rock color and topography. The oil mining industries are the largest purchasers of Landsat data and most of the new fossil-fuel finds owe their detection to a Landsat picture. One early revelation was that oil and gas deposits on the Alaska North Slope were far greater than at first thought. By scanning the large folds and ruptures in the Earth's crust, Landsat gives the geologists helpful clues to the siting of deposits.

Orbit 3. Mapping mission. Before Landsat, more than half of Asia, Africa and Latin America had not been mapped at scales larger than 1:1,000,000. The satellites have allowed quick and economical mapping of previously uncharted areas and have updated and corrected existing maps. A new geological map of Egypt was undertaken by Landsat in half the time and a fraction of the cost it would otherwise have involved.

Orbit 4. Forest conservation exercise. Knowing the volume of timber across large forest areas clearly helps in designing a conservation policy and in deciding on the best cutting plans. In Brazil, Landsat pictures have been used to control forest development and to police the tree-cutting activities of private foresters and land owners.

Orbit 5. Forest fire warning. In a Canadian survey using Landsat information, 42 burns were traced

Left: The Red Sea and Gulf of Aden, taken from 400 miles above the Earth by Landsat D's infrared camera. Landsat and its companion satellites provide geologists with invaluable information about the movement of the Earth's crust. This photograph, for example, reveals that the Red Sea has been gradually opening up each year.

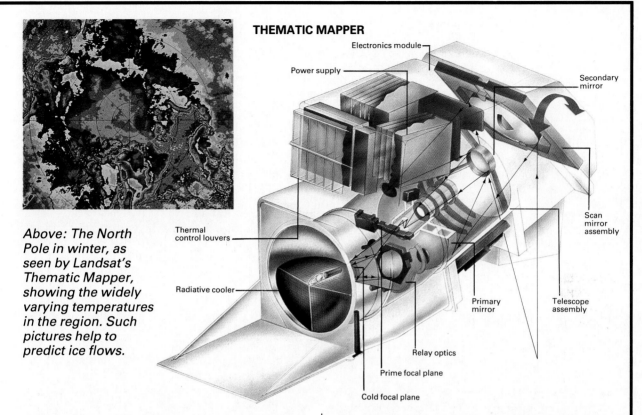

THEMATIC MAPPER

Electronics module

Power supply

Secondary mirror

Scan mirror assembly

Thermal control louvers

Radiative cooler

Primary mirror

Telescope assembly

Relay optics

Prime focal plane

Cold focal plane

Above: The North Pole in winter, as seen by Landsat's Thematic Mapper, showing the widely varying temperatures in the region. Such pictures help to predict ice flows.

across northern Saskatchewan and the extent of damage monitored.

Orbit 6. Tracking of wild animals. In an extensive National Park Survey, scientists in Colorado used Landsat to match the needs of wild animals with the park's resources in numerous remote areas.

Orbit 7. Ocean sweep. Information is beamed from buoys out at sea to the receiving satellite providing details on local air and water surface temperature, salinity, the height of waves and the speed of surface currents. The modern trawler can use this information to predict where fish are most likely to school, and to pinpoint dense areas of plankton in upwelling areas.

Orbit 8. Surveillance of ice. By making forecasts of snow and sea ice, ships are able to reroute for greater safety and economy.

Orbit 9. Report on urban areas. Areas of concentrated urbanization and even traffic show up quite clearly on Landsat pictures. Town planners can use this information in planning industrial development and routing arterial systems.

Orbit 10. Pollution report. Smog clouds over major cities are visible reminders that a global watch must be kept on atmospheric pollution. A device in the satellite called a correlation interferometer keeps check on the levels of carbon monoxide in the various layers of the atmosphere.

Above: With 100 different detectors, seven spectral bands, and a radiometric precision of 256 levels, the Landsat's Thematic Mapper is a highly versatile tool for gathering data.

Orbit 11. Snow-melt early warning. Through photography of snow-covered ground and mountains, Landsat has made the prediction of water from snow melts reliable – important to hydroelectric power plants, irrigation schemes and flood control.

Orbit 12. Earthquake watch. The satellites keep up a routine communication with Earth-based geodetic stations sited along earthquake fault zones and transmit their warnings.

Orbit 13. Harvest forecast. The accurate prediction of the world's grain harvests and the discoveries of new farming land being made possible by Landsat could improve millions of lives and save millions of dollars.

Orbit 14. Drought warning. Prolonged drought in the Sahel, a huge area of African grassland just south of the Sahara Desert, caused starvation on a tragic scale. Landsat pictures proved that lack of grazing rotation and livestock management were allowing desert encroachment and causing dust-bowl conditions.

They are just some of the missions a Landsat or Seasat satellite might be required to complete.

Schlieren techniques

Many problems of science and engineering involve substances which are colorless, transparent and nonluminous, so that their observation by direct visual or photographic methods is difficult. Examples are the motion of air past models of aircraft wings, problems of convection, the mixing of liquids or gases, and detecting of faults in windows.

In such cases the phenomena that are of interest frequently involve changes of *refraction index*. The refractive index of a material is simply the ratio of the speed of light in a vacuum to the speed of light in the material. It is a measure of how much the material will bend a light ray traversing it. Several methods are available for revealing small changes in refractive index, and those most frequently adopted are called schlieren methods because they were originally used in Germany for detecting regions of enhanced density in optical glass which are often in the form of streaks (German *Schliere*).

Suppose that a beam of light is passed through a transparent material in which the refractive index changes at right angles to the beam. The beam will be deflected by refraction from its undisturbed path. In schlieren methods several techniques may be used to detect these deflections and enable changes in refractive index to be observed or recorded.

The arrangement of the apparatus depends on the nature and scale of the phenomena to be observed. Assume that the experiment is two dimensional, in other words imagine that the event to be studied is contained between flat parallel windows perpendicular to the light beam, and that between these windows the conditions are constant along the undisturbed path of each light ray. This situation would, for example, occur approximately in a wind tunnel experiment if a model of the section of an aircraft wing completely spanned the wind tunnel in a direction parallel to the light beam between glass windows in the side walls. Lenses or mirrors may be used as the main optical components, and it will be assumed here that mirrors are used because if a light beam of large diameter is required mirrors are easier and cheaper to manufacture.

A concave mirror has a focal point, to which all parallel rays of light coming in along its axis are reflected, forming an image. If this situation is reversed, and a point source of light is placed at the focus, it will produce a beam of parallel light just like a searchlight. In practice, the mirror is tilted slightly so that the light source lies outside the parallel reflected beam. If a second concave mirror is now used to intercept the parallel light, it will form an image of the point source at its focus.

If the aircraft wing section is located between the two mirrors, it is possible to form an image of it by

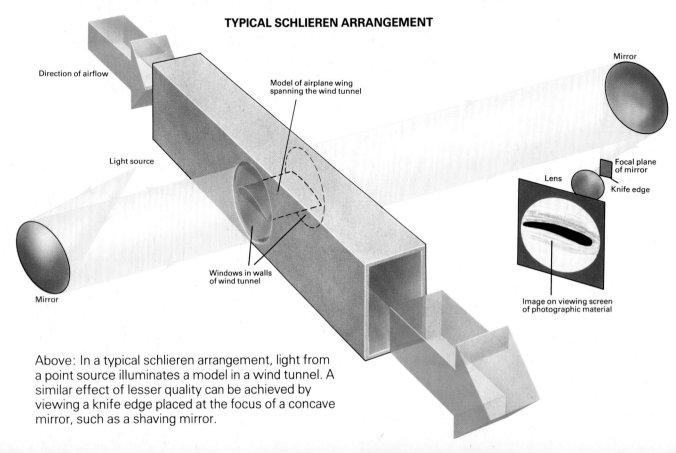

TYPICAL SCHLIEREN ARRANGEMENT

Direction of airflow

Model of airplane wing spanning the wind tunnel

Mirror

Light source

Focal plane of mirror

Lens

Knife edge

Windows in walls of wind tunnel

Image on viewing screen of photographic material

Mirror

Above: In a typical schlieren arrangement, light from a point source illuminates a model in a wind tunnel. A similar effect of lesser quality can be achieved by viewing a knife edge placed at the focus of a concave mirror, such as a shaving mirror.

putting a lens beyond the image of the light source and to project the wing section's image to a viewing screen or photographic film. Because the light between the two mirrors is parallel, each point around the wing section itself can be considered to form a separate image of the light source at the focal point of the second mirror. If the light is undisturbed on its path, all these images will coincide, producing a point image. But if there are variations in the refractive index gradient (such as those caused by changes in air density and pressure as air flows across the wing section), some light rays will be deflected slightly and will not come to the same focal point as the rest of the light. They will, however, be imaged by the lens in the normal way.

Because the light has been displaced, and because the displacement is evident at the image in front of the lens, it is possible to reveal the deviations which have taken place. A sharp straight edge, usually called a *knife edge*, is placed at the focal point of the second mirror in such a way that if there were no deviations, most of the light would reach the viewing screen, the total intensity being slightly reduced. If, however, the light is deflected, it may be blocked off completely by the knife edge, or will pass completely unhindered. In the first case the image of the wing at a certain point will be reduced in brightness, and in the second case it will be increased. In this way, the slightest deviation of light across the wing section will show up as a lighter or darker region. A rectangular light source of small size is used for this arrangement. If instead of a knife edge an optical filter with bands of different colors is used, deflection of the light rays will displace the image onto a different band of the filter, so that the color of the light on the viewing screen changes to the observer.

Practical uses

By using discharge tubes, spark gaps or pulsed lasers as light sources, exposure times well below a millionth of a second can be produced for schlieren photography, and various techniques are available for motion picture photography. So these methods may be used to study rapidly moving phenomena such as explosion waves or the shock waves produced by projectiles moving at high speeds. They produce no disturbances to the flow field or other event, and are limited only by the size of the optical components. Typical systems use mirrors 1 ft (0.3 m) to 3 ft (1 m) in diameter.

A similar system, the *Foucault test*, used in optics production, tests not the refractive index of the air but the quality of a single mirror. Errors on the mirror surface produce easily visible effects using this system.

See also: Light; Mirror; Optics; Wind tunnel.

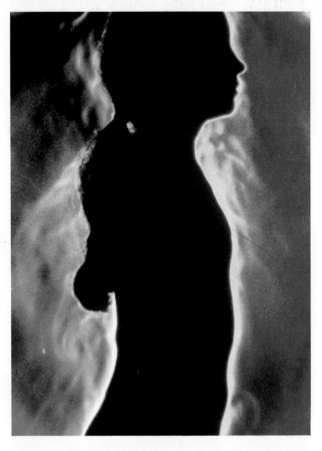

Above: A schlieren photograph of the Vortex formed by a fan spinning over an alcohol lamp.
Below: This schlieren photograph of a girl shows the thin layer of air attached to her skin.

Schmidt camera

Schmidt cameras or telescopes are probably the most sensitive optical systems which it is possible to devise for high quality photography. They are used when good images over a wide field of view are required at low light levels. In astronomy, the wide field of view has made the Schmidt telescope the principal instrument for carrying out photographic surveys of the night sky.

A spherical mirror forms good images on its axis from light striking its central regions. However, light striking the outer regions of such a mirror is focused at a different point on the mirror's axis. This problem, known as *spherical aberration*, gets worse as mirrors with faster *f-ratios* are used: that is, as the diameter becomes large compared with the focal length, giving brighter images.

A simple solution is to alter the spherical surface to a *paraboloid*, a figure slightly deeper in the center than a sphere, thus eliminating spherical aberra-tion entirely. The penalty is that off-axis images suffer badly from another type of distortion, or aber-ration, known as *coma*. A more satisfactory solution consists of combining a spherical mirror with a cor-recting lens of some sort.

The German Bernhard Schmidt realized in 1932 that if the correcting lens was placed at the center of curvature of the mirror, off-axis rays would be able to produce almost as good images as on-axis rays, and that such a system could have a wide-angle field of view. This system, with a corrector at the center of curvature, is called a Schmidt camera.

The focal plane in a Schmidt camera lies midway between the corrector and the mirror but is curved with its center at the center of curvature of the mirror, that is, at the corrector. The photographic emulsion recording the image in the camera must be bent accurately to this surface. The two largest Schmidt cameras in present use, both of focal ratio *f*/2.5 with mirrors 72 in. (1.8 m) in diameter and corrector plates 48 in. (1.2 m) in diameter, are located at Mount Palomar in California and at

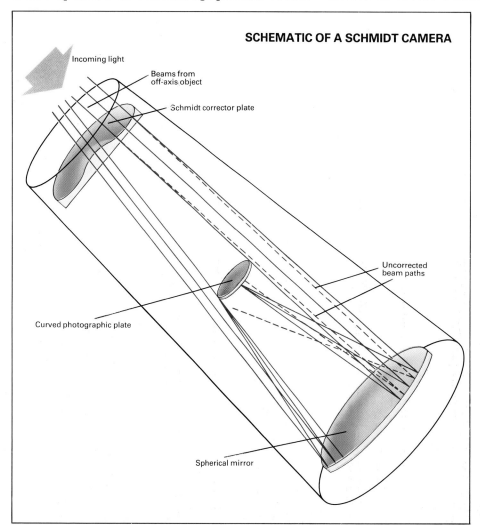

SCHEMATIC OF A SCHMIDT CAMERA

Incoming light

Beams from off-axis object

Schmidt corrector plate

Uncorrected beam paths

Curved photographic plate

Spherical mirror

Left: Light entering a Schmidt camera passes through a corrector plate which insures the image is sharply focused. Without the corrector plate, the light would follow the dotted path and fail to focus clearly on the photographic plate, because of the spherical aberration of the mirror. The design of the corrector plate used in the Schmidt camera deviates light by the correct amount to bring both on-axis and off-axis rays to the same focal point, although the focal plane is curved.

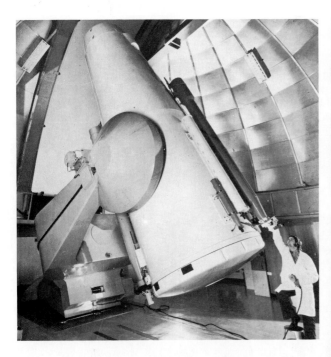

Above: The 48-in. (1.2-m) Schmidt in Australia being used for a southern sky survey. The use of large Schmidt cameras has been as important to astronomy as the use of large telescopes, because they cover expansive areas of the sky. Detail is then studied by large telescopes.

Above: This mass of glowing hydrogen gas, viewed by the Mount Palomar Schmidt camera, is known as the North America Nebula, because of its faintly misty shape. A single photograph taken with a large Schmidt camera may show more than a million stars, each sharply defined.

Siding Spring Observatory in New South Wales, Australia. A smaller version, with a corrector plate 39 in. (1 m) diameter, is at the European Southern Observatory in Chile. In all these cameras, the center of the photographic plates protrudes almost 0.4 in. (10 mm) in front of the corners. The bending, handling and uniform manufacture of such large, thin, plates are not trivial problems.

These three large Schmidt cameras have fields of six degrees in diameter (12 times that of the Moon). They are being used to survey vast areas of the sky in great detail, enabling interesting objects to be located for study with large telescopes. Their wide fields are suitable for finding the relative positions of objects; the entire Northern Hemisphere was recorded on photographic plates by the 48 in. (1.2 m) Schmidt at Mount Palomar in California. Plates of the Mount Palomar Sky Survey, as it was known, are now standard references for astronomers the world over.

A camera with aperture (corrector plate diameter) 17 in. (432 mm) and having a field of 50 degrees has been developed to track meteors and artificial satellites. The focal plane here was so curved that specially molded film had to be manufactured.

The correcting lens in a Schmidt camera is usually a thin, nonspherical corrector plate (3.9 in., 100 mm, thick for the 48 in. Schmidt cameras), but solid Schmidt cameras can be made, in which the corrector and mirror are made from one piece of glass, with the corrector surface figured on one end and the spherical mirror figured and aluminized (coated to make it reflective) on the other. A slot is cut out in the middle to accept the film. The speed of such cameras is phenomenal; they can be made as fast as the theoretical limit of $f/0.5$ without unacceptable degradation of image quality. But solid Schmidt cameras can only be made small because of the difficulty of manufacturing a large flawless piece of glass; they also suffer severely from CHROMATIC ABERRATION. They have found applications as the camera in spectrographs where single-color images of lines are formed and chromatic aberration is no disadvantage.

See also: Astronomical telescope; Camera; Lens; Photographic processing; Solar system; Space photography; Telescope.

Screw manufacture

The origins of the screw are not known exactly, but some types of screw devices such as the screw auger (a kind of drill) and the ARCHIMEDEAN SCREW were in use in Greece and Egypt before the third century BC. By the first century BC, heavy wooden screws were used in presses for making wine and olive oil, and the character of the screw had thus been given a new dimension and was used to exert a force, its modern counterpart being called a *power screw* or *screw jack*. Metal screws and nuts first appeared in the fifteenth century, and can be seen in some medieval armor.

In the U.S. during the nineteenth century, David Wilkinson designed and built his screw-cutting lathe and later, in 1845, Stephen Fitch built the first *turret lathe*, specifically to produce screws for an arms contract. Shortly after the American Civil War, Christopher Walker invented the completely automatic lathe solely to make screws to improve the assembly of his repeating rifles. As with many other inventions, the development of the lathe was largely inspired by the production of weapons.

A screw consists of a circular cylindrical barrel onto which is formed a spiral ridge which is generally of roughly triangular cross section. There are two broad categories, *machine screws* and *wood screws*. Both are generally made of metal but whereas the machine screw is of constant diameter and mates with a threaded *nut* or hole, the wood screw tapers to a point and the wood into which it is turned is deformed into a mating thread. The latter must usually be started in a hole made by an awl or a drill. The principle of operation in both cases is that as the screw is turned the spiral thread translates the rotation into an axial movement. This ability in fact leads to other uses of the screw than just fasteners. The lead screw on a lathe or the screw micrometer are examples of the screw being used to transfer power or provide axial measurement.

There are many varieties of machine screw or *bolt* used to clamp machine parts together, either in conjunction with a nut or with a threaded hole. These

Below: High-quality screws for use in aircraft are made on an automatic lathe.

screws stretch when tightened, so that the axial tensile load thereby created holds the parts together. The heads of smaller screws are generally made with screwdriver slots, Phillips type heads, or hexagonal recesses to take an Allen key. The larger types almost invariably have hexagonal heads to which very large torques can be applied with either open-ended or box-end wrenches.

Threads

Although there is a large number of different thread forms to suit various requirements, the basic thread form used in the U.S. is the Unified Thread series developed in association with Britain and Canada. In this series the *Unified Coarse* (UNC) threads are recommended for general use, the *Unified Fine* (UNF) threads being used where the screw is subjected to strong vibration or where extra strength is required. Metric threads are finding increasing application and generally conform to the International Standards Organization (ISO) standards.

Self-tapping screw

Beside the woodscrew and the machine screw there is a third class of screw fastener, namely the *self-tapping* screw. This forms its own mating thread in such materials as metals, plastics, glass-reinforced plastics, asbestos and resin-impregnated plywood, when driven into a drilled hole of which the diameter is less than the overall diameter of the screw. The threads are formed in the hole by the displacement of material adjacent to the hole so that it flows around the screw. A further refinement of this type is the *thread-cutting* tapping screw, which has cutting edges and chip cavities which produce a mating thread by removing material.

Screw jacks

Screws that modify force and motion are known as power screws, one form being the screw jack which converts torque (turning movement) to thrust. In one version, the thrust, used to lift a heavy object, is created by turning the screw in a stationary nut. By using a long bar to turn the screw, a small force at the end of the bar can create a large thrust force, and the screw jack can then be said to have a high *mechanical advantage*.

Screw production

The production of screws by machining is a fairly limited technique, employed only on fasteners of unusual design or those too small or too large to be processed by other methods. Both standard automatic lathes and special automatic screw machines are employed, using hexagonal or round stock in cut lengths. Although finish is excellent, machining of screws is slow and wasteful of metal.

Screws are produced in a wide range of sizes, head

THREAD FORMING

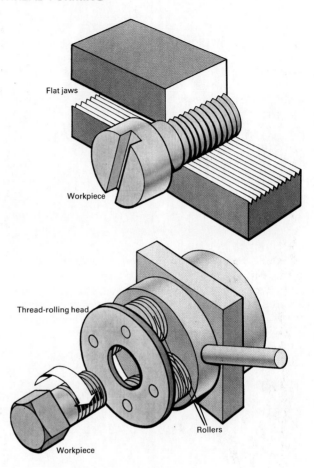

Above: In the reciprocal method of thread forming, the screw blank is rolled between two flat dies; in the cylindrical method, it is turned within a circular arrangement of rollers.

styles and materials, all of which are determined by their applications. Until quite recently, the thread forms were equally numerous and this created problems in both standardization and manufacture. Accordingly, in 1966 the International Standards Organization proposed the restriction of threads to ISO metric and inch, coarse and fine *pitches* in what is known as the preferred range of sizes. These proposals have been generally adopted throughout the world and the advantages to manufacturing are considerable. The pitch, also called *basic pitch*, is the distance between a point on one thread to the corresponding point on the next thread. Pitch is also taken to mean the number of threads per inch or per centimeter. For example, the Unified Standard pitches for a ¼ in. screw are ¼ 20 (coarse), ¼ 28 (fine) and ¼ 32 (extra fine).

Screws are made from specific heading qualities of low to medium carbon steel wire, stainless steel,

Above: In a double-blow cold-heading machine, two strokes of the ram produce one screw blank, which the machine then ejects.
Below: A multistation transfer heading machine works like a series of single-blow, single-die headers, all linked up by a transfer mechanism.

nickel alloys, brass and aluminum alloy. Although some of these materials are more difficult to process than others, the production methods remain much the same.

Cold heading

Cold heading is a widely used method of forming or *upsetting* a head of predetermined size and shape on one end of a cut blank of rod or wire. Production is a relatively high speed continuous process; the wire is fed from coil mounted on a *swift* or *payoff* unit. The end of the coil may be welded to the end of the next one. The wire passes through a pre-straightening unit into the machine where, in a predetermined sequence, it is cut to the correct length and, depending on the number of blows required to form the head, it is punched into a tungsten-carbide die so that the head takes up the required shape, for example, hexagonal, round, recessed, and so on. After forming, the blank is automatically ejected into a receiver for further processing.

The two basic types of cold heading machines are those fitted with split (open) dies and solid (closed) dies. Split dyes are used for making screws or parts with wide tolerances and greater than average lengths; solid dies are designed to achieve greater accuracy (close tolerances) and also allow a degree of extrusion, that is, a reduction in the shank diameter of the screw blank. This extrusion, which is achieved within the die, is necessary so that when the threads are rolled into the metal at a later stage of production, the correct major diameter is accomplished. For screw manufacture the cold heading machines are also classified as either single blow or double blow. The single blow header applies the heading punch once for each revolution of the machine's flywheel to produce one screw for each stroke of the punch ram. The double blow header is fitted with an indexing head containing two punches, each of which is applied once during the cycle. Thus, two strokes of the ram are required to produce one screw blank. As an alternative, the die itself may be indexed automatically instead of the punch. Production speeds, depending on the diameter and length of the screw, can range from about 100 to 550 parts per minute.

A more advanced type of cold header is the transfer machine, which is rather like a series of single blow, single die headers, each linked to the other by means of a transfer mechanism. In this machine the blank is ejected from the die after each blow, to be transferred to the next station for progressive forming. One of the advantages of this type is that trimming, reduction and pointing are carried out in the one machine.

There are many advantages of cold heading, including the high volume of production achieved and the complete elimination of material wastage. (Because of this, cold heading is called a chipless method of production.) Also, cold heading causes the metal grain flow to follow the contours of the head, thus avoiding stress, particularly where the underside of the head joins the shank. The process allows the use of low-carbon steels for highly stressed application because the cold working which takes place during heading actually improves the mechanical qualities of the metal.

Disadvantages of the method are generally restricted to size. For example, very small or very large screws tend to be uneconomic, the former due to handling problems and the latter because large screws demand large and powerful machines.

The intermediate stages between cold heading of the screws and the thread rolling operation may include slotting of the head, trimming and pointing.

Thread rolling

Thread rolling is also a cold forming process. The thread form is impressed in the screw shank by rolling it in a single operation under controlled pressure between two hardened dies having the reverse profile of the specified thread. The indentation of the die thread crests causes the metal to fill the area between the thread flanks by *plastic deformation*. Since no metal is removed from the screw blank, but is only displaced, the blank diameter on which the thread is rolled must be slightly undersize, about equal to the thread *pitch diameter*.

The pitch diameter is also called the *simple effective diameter*. It is the diameter of an imaginary cylinder, the surface of which would pass through the thread profiles at such a point as to make the width of the remaining groove equal to one half the basic pitch. On a *perfect thread* (where the groove and the thread are the same size) this will be the point at which the widths of the thread and the groove are equal.

There are three types of thread rolling processes, the flat (reciprocating) die, the centerless cylindrical die and the *planetary* rotary die. The first two processes have production speeds in the range 60 to 250 parts per minute, depending on blank diameter, while the planetary die type achieves speeds of between 60 and 2000 parts per minute. In the reciprocating die method, there are two flat dies, one of which is stationary while the other reciprocates, rolling the screw blank between them. With centerless cylindrical dies, there are two or three round dies and the blank is rolled between them. In the planetary die method the blank is held while the dies roll around it.

In most thread rolling operations, the screw blanks are fed automatically to the dies down a guide chute from a vibrating hopper feeder which insures that the blanks are correctly presented and at the correct feed rate.

Although the point is frequently argued, the rolled screw thread is superior to the cut thread, since it has the same characteristics as a cold headed product in that the fibers of the metal follow the contour of the thread and are not discontinued or severed as in the case of cut threads. The roots of rolled threads are stressed in compression, thus improving the fatigue strength, particularly in medium-carbon steels.

See also: Nail manufacture; Rolling, metal.

Above: The feed device to a thread-rolling machine feeds the screw blanks to the dies.
Below: The thread-rolling machine forms threads by rolling the screw between two dies.

Below: In a head slotting machine, screw blanks are clamped in grooves around the perimeter of a wheel, which slowly revolves as a circular cutter makes a slot of predetermined width.

Seaplane and amphibian

The practice of flying aircraft off water is almost as old as aviation itself and results from the number of good natural runways available from the world's rivers, lakes and harbors. It releases the aircraft from its greatest limitation, the need for specially prepared strips of ground for take-off and landing. If, however, the seaplane is fitted with retractable wheels to exploit landing strips as well, it becomes the truly liberated *amphibian*.

The true water plane is the *flying boat*, with the fuselage itself designed to operate on water with most of the characteristics of a boat. Most small landplanes can be fitted with minihulls or floats instead of wheels and, as such, earn the separate designation of *floatplane*.

The first recorded successful flight from water was made in March 1910 by Henri Fabre of France, just over six years after the Wright brothers achieved the first sustained powered flight of a heavier-than-air aircraft. The aircraft, with its three flat-bottomed floats, was primitive, but it initiated two decades of aircraft evolution in which seaplanes played the leading role.

The next step, in 1911, introduced one of the great names of seaplane development when Glenn Curtiss of the U.S. flew a novel craft with a single float – to which wheels were soon added to produce the first amphibian. His first real flying boat came out the following year, and suddenly seaplanes gained acceptance. In 1914 the world's first scheduled airline began in Florida, operating between St Petersburg and Tampa, using Benoist flying boats.

From 1913 to 1931 were the years of the famous Schneider Trophy races for seaplanes, whose role in stimulating high-performance technology is reflected in the progress of winning average speeds from 47.75 mph (76.8 km/h) for the first meeting to 340 mph (547 km/h) for the last. The final winner, Britain's Supermarine S.6B, later set a world record of 407 mph (655 km/h), and evolved directly into the Spitfire of World War II fame.

Britain's efforts, in fact, led seaplane develop-

Below: A Canadair water bomber, a firefighting seaplane which fills its water tanks when skimming along the surface of a lake.
Right: The water is mixed with a chemical to form a smothering foamy-white blanket, which is released onto a forest fire.

ments of all kinds through the 1920s and early 1930s, culminating in the huge Short Sarafand of 1935 which, with its 215 ft (65.7 m) wingspan, was the largest ever biplane. But, by then, such devotion to biplanes had already cost Britain the lead, as faster monoplane flying boats were developed in Europe and the U.S. Germany's 12-engined Dornier Do.X, although never entering service, introduced the age of the giants, dominated by the great Sikorsky boats and Martin Clippers of America. Finally came the Boeing 314 Clipper which, in 1939, established scheduled transatlantic passenger services. Largest of all was Howard Hughes' 460,000 lb (208,650 kg) Hercules, with a 320 ft (97.54 m) wingspan, which made its first and only flight in 1947, and could have carried 700 passengers. It is the largest aircraft ever to fly, with an overall length of 219 ft (66.75 m).

Among the most famous aircraft of World War II are America's Consolidated Catalina and Britain's Short Sunderland flying boats, used unceasingly for maritime patrol in the Atlantic and the Pacific Oceans. 1953 saw the appearance of the British 310,000 lb (140,610 kg) Saunders Roe Princess, the last of the giants and which never entered service. But several attempts were made at building smaller, jet flying boats, notably the beautiful Saunders Roe SR-A1 fighter and the four-engined Martin P.6M Seamaster.

Design
Water is as demanding an element as the air. Seaplane pilots must also become sailors. Likewise, seaplane designers must understand hydrodynamics as well as aerodynamics. Both must appreciate the complex forces of water and wind on water. The variations and conflicts in design, both past and present, are as numerous as those of the boat industry.

The aerodynamic factors differ little except for a preference for keeping wings, tailplane and engines high and as far as possible from spray. The seaplane's greater bulk forward usually calls for a larger vertical tail area to control it. But the landing floats require unique considerations, such as good flotation and stability, ruggedness and lightness plus hydrodynamic lift with minimal spray.

Below: The Lake Buccaneer amphibian has a fully retractable wheeled undercarriage for use on land, and wing floats to provide stability on water. Steering on land is by means of the nose wheel, and a retractable rudder is used for steering on water. The engine pod is mounted on the fuselage to prevent water ingress.

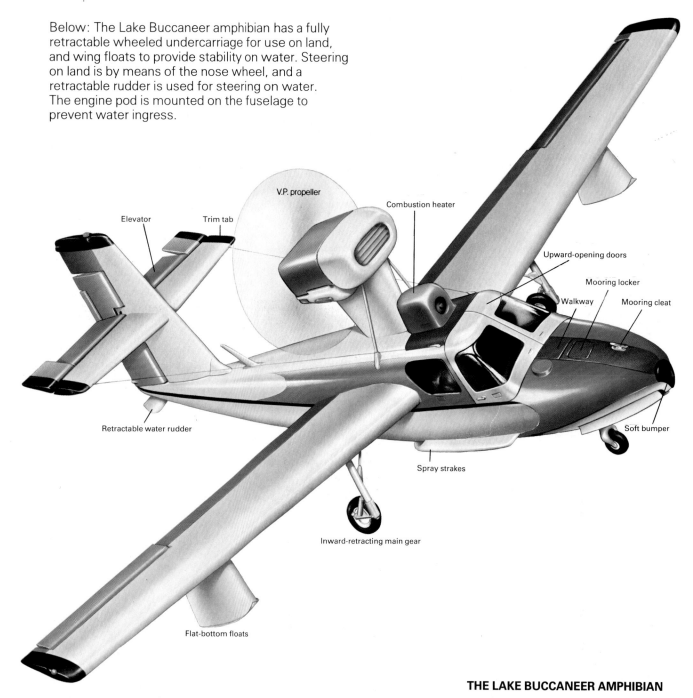

Elevator
Trim tab
V.P. propeller
Combustion heater
Upward-opening doors
Mooring locker
Walkway
Mooring cleat
Retractable water rudder
Soft bumper
Spray strakes
Inward-retracting main gear
Flat-bottom floats

THE LAKE BUCCANEER AMPHIBIAN

A flying boat, like an ordinary boat, must have its center of buoyancy beneath its center of gravity (cg), enough displacement for its gross weight, enough freeboard to prevent swamping and a high bow for low-speed taxiing. It differs only in the greater stability offered by wing-tip floats or other outrigger-type stabilizers and which compensate for a high cg and a minimal keel.

For take-off, the hull must rise quickly out of the water and start planing like a speedboat if flying speed is to be attained, and so the hull bottom is designed to push the water downward. A shallow V-shaped bottom is now almost standard, often slightly concave to flatten out the spray and improve lift. Fluted bottoms with an intermediate *chine* or ridge running between keel and side improve these characteristics and are now popular on floats and small flying boats.

Unlike a speedboat, where the cg is near the stern or *transom*, an aircraft also needs hull support well behind the cg, to cope with displacement when at rest and to give lift during early acceleration. So

Above: A Short Sunderland maritime rescue and antisubmarine flying boat used during World War II. It has a top speed of 210 mph (338 km/h).
Below: A Short Calcutta flying boat which went into service in 1928. It was of all-metal construction and carried 15 passengers.

slightly behind the cg, the flying boat hull has a sharp up-break called the *step*, corresponding to the transom of a boat. The step reduces skin friction on the hull afterbody while planing and allows the aircraft to tilt up at lift-off to achieve a suitable flying angle for the wings. When planing, the airplane is described as being on the step and can also taxi at speed in this mode with low throttle setting while maneuvering tightly yet safely.

The floats fitted to landplanes to convert them into floatplanes are little more than small, sealed hulls. Modern floats also have some aerodynamic shape to give lift and reduce the weight penalty. Twin floats are now standard, although a single float was popular before the war and a tail float was carried on some early seaplanes. The high stance of floatplanes, however, gives them a high cg and sensitivity to crosswinds.

Helicopters, not needing hydrodynamic gear, are often fitted with light, inflated-rubber pontoons or have these strapped to landing skids ready for inflation by compressed gas. Some larger modern helicopters even have full boat hulls for amphibious operation. A new concept now under test exploits vertical *sponsons* to provide a smoother ride in heavy seas for air-sea rescue craft. Fixed-wing aircraft could swivel such floats to the horizontal for take-off and landing. Possible use of lightweight water skis and hydrofoils has also been receiving attention in recent years.

See also: Aerodynamics; Aircraft; Airplane; Hydrodynamics; Sailing technology.

Sea rescue

In the West, the first steps toward establishing sea rescue services were taken at the end of the eighteenth century, although by that time the Chinese had already been operating red boats (specially built rescue boats) for several hundred years. Initial efforts were concentrated on building unsinkable open boats, the first lifeboats, which were fitted with buoyancy tanks to keep them afloat. A boat of this type was successfully tested in France in 1765 and another was constructed in Britain in 1785. In the U.S., a lifeboat equipped with hydrogen-filled buoyancy tanks was designed and constructed in 1816.

Today, most seafaring nations have some system for making rescues at sea, whether operated by volunteers, government agencies or the armed forces. One of the earliest such organizations was the British Royal National Lifeboat Institution which was formed in 1824 and is still funded by voluntary contributions with most of the crew members also being volunteers. In the U.S., the responsibility for sea rescue operations lies with the Coast Guard which took over the duties of the older Life Saving Service when it was established in 1915. In many countries the efforts of such services are supplemented by the armed forces who have the equipment and trained personnel to carry out large-scale Search and Rescue (SAR) operations.

Techniques

When a vessel or individual requires rescue, the immediate action is to attract attention. This action may be done by firing distress flares or by radio, while the alarm may also be raised by other observers – this is often the case when people get into trouble inshore. Most rescue organizations maintain a constant radio watch on the distress frequencies so that they can respond as quickly as possible.

Other vessels may be able to provide assistance or pass on the distress call but usually it is the onshore coastguard who receives the message or spots the flares and alerts the appropriate rescue service. Generally, a helicopter or a lifeboat is alerted, though these services frequently work together. On long searches, such as when a vessel is reported missing, fixed wing aircraft may also be used together with surface ships.

Rescue by helicopter can be quicker than by lifeboat, and if the rescued person is injured minutes may be vital. Lifeboats are able to stay out longer without refueling and can take people from vessels which helicopters are unable to approach because of masts, rigging or fires; they are also better able to effect searches and rescues at night. They can also carry more people and where large numbers are involved a helicopter may transfer the

Below: Survivors of an Argentinian attack on British landing ships come ashore in lifeboats during the Falklands War in 1982.

Right: Submersibles such as Pisces are essential for underwater surveys, maintenance of structures at depth, as well as salvage and rescue. The Pisces can lift objects from the ocean floor by an external remote-controlled arm. Pisces I was the first submersible to start work in the North Sea, in 1969. Since then, their use has been extended considerably. Below right: Divers preparing to retrieve a submersible from the sea during bad weather conditions.

survivors to a lifeboat so that it can continue the rescue operation without having to return to land.

Lifeboats are normally based in one place and may lie afloat, be launched down a slipway or transported on a carriage down to the sea. The carriage launch uses specially designed tractors with watertight engines. The tractors may be submerged up to the driver's neck without stalling, as the air intake and exhaust pipes are extended above this level. In some countries, such as Norway, there are some cruising lifeboats which accompany fishing fleets, and these have living accommodation on board.

Once at the scene of the casualty the coxswain of the lifeboat must quickly assess the situation and decide which equipment will best help. The main purposes of lifeboat equipment are to help a lifeboat to reach a casualty, to allow survivors to be taken off, to maintain communications with other vessels, aircraft and the shore, and to give protection to the survivors and the crew. One of the great advances in sea rescue has been in communications. To maintain liaison between the shore, the sea and the air, VHF and MF radio equipment is used.

Helicopter rescue

Helicopter rescues are made using a winch system with the helicopter hovering above the vessel and lowering a cable with a sling to pick up the survivors one at a time and take them into the helicopter. Frequently, a crew member is first lowered to the ship to take charge of the operation. Stretcher systems can be used for casualties, again with a helicopter crew member being lifted along with the casualty to control the movement of the stretcher.

Problems can arise when deck cranes and the superstructure prevent the helicopter from taking

Left: A 44 ft (13 m) Coast Guard lifeboat attempts a rescue in rough seas off the coast of Florida.
Right: For some rescue missions, helicopters are the best means of transportation. Equipped with a rescue basket and winch, they can respond quickly and fly long distances to the scene of accidents. Helicopters are also used by the Coast Guard to patrol the coastline and prevent people from getting into difficulties.

up a suitable position and coniderable demands are placed on the flying skill of the pilot, especially in adverse weather conditions. Individuals can also be lifted direct from the sea or from lifeboats and rafts.

Shore rescue

When a ship is in difficulties or aground on the shore the survivors may be taken off using *breeches buoy* equipment. A rocket is used to carry a light line from the shore to the vessel and the crew uses this line to pull over the main cable and a pulley block system which are secured to the ship, the other end of the cable being similarly secured on shore. The breeches buoy itself consists of a canvas seat arrangement in which one of the survivors sits and is pulled to shore along the fixed cable, with the buoy being returned repeatedly until everyone has been taken off the ship.

Lifeboats

Some of the modern lifeboat's equipment is traditional and has been proved by years of experience. The *drogue*, a hooped canvas cone streamed from the stern of the boat to steady it when it is running before a sea, and the breeches buoy are familiar items. The *echo sounder*, which tells a coxswain the exact depth of water under the boat, and the radio direction finders are among the items of electronic equipment. For some years after the invention of radar, no sets were available for boats so low in the water as lifeboats, but today radar is one of several items fitted as standard.

Recent constructional development of lifeboats has brought several completely new concepts. Designs have always been tied to the requirements of strength and ability to stand the worst weathers, because lifeboats put to sea when other vessels are seeking shelter. This has meant the incorporation of airtight buoyancy compartments in the hulls, so that if the hull is holed in several places, the lifeboat will remain afloat. One of the great controversies, which raged until recently, concerned *self-righting* – the ability of a boat to right itself in the event it capsizes. Self-righting lifeboats of the last century were not liked by many crews, as the main buoyancy for righting was provided by high *end boxes*. These could not be built too high, otherwise they obstructed vision, so the boats had to be kept fairly narrow, reducing their initial stability and increasing the tendency to capsize.

Modern self-righting lifeboats have even greater stability than the non-self-righters designed between the World Wars, and rely on the buoyant force provided by watertight compartments, including the engine casing and superstructure. Although the first boats to have this sort of righting arrangement also had a system of water ballast transfer, this is no longer necessary, because watertight cabins and additional closed watertight doors have been introduced. A second departure from conventional designs has been new hull forms which have greatly increased the speeds of lifeboats. For example, a 44 ft (13.4 m) steel-hulled lifeboat developed in the U.S. has been widely adopted by other countries.

Capable of speeds of about 15 knots, it is exceptionally maneuverable. The larger, 52 ft (15.9 m), Arun class lifeboat, initially built in wood, is being constructed in GRP (glass-reinforced plastic or glass fiber). This new material for large lifeboats had to be stringently studied before acceptance. Boats of this class have speeds in excess of 20 knots, are self-righting and, like the 44 ft lifeboats, lie afloat. They have double-skinned hulls, the spaces between the inner and outer skins being filled with expanded polyurethane foam which keeps the lifeboat afloat even if all 26 of the watertight compartments are holed at the same time.

The superstructure is made of welded aluminum and the seats in the wheelhouse for the five crew members are equipped with safety belts. The vessel can be controlled either from the wheelhouse or from a *flying bridge* above the wheelhouse. Access to the wheelhouse is through a coffer dam entrance which has two doors, as in an airlock, to prevent flooding if the vessel should capsize.

One of the limitations of these boats is that they cannot be launched down slipways. Coastlines vary greatly, and in many places there will be no harbor with a sufficient depth of water at all states of the tide to moor a lifeboat afloat, and so a slipway is necessary.

To protect the screws and prevent CAVITATION, a certain hull form, with propellers in tunnels, has until recently been necessary, but the new Tyne class lifeboat with a semiplaning hull is capable of speeds up to 18 knots.

Some rescue services also use large vessels which can spend extended periods at sea. For example, the U.S. Coast Guard Reliance class cutters have a range of 6000 miles (9700 km) and are specially designed for search-and-rescue operations. Special features include a bridge with 360° visibility and a helicopter flight deck, and they are also able to tow ships of up to 10,000 tons.

Inshore rescue

One of the most important recent innovations in sea rescue techniques has been the development of inshore lifeboats. Increasing numbers of people in all developed countries are taking their leisure on the sea, and naturally some of them get into difficulties. Small dinghies, yachts, swimmers and children on air beds may all need very quick assistance and therefore inshore lifeboats were introduced.

Inshore lifeboats can be launched quickly from a beach and are capable of high speeds once in the water. A typcal design, the Atlantic 21, can reach about 29 knots, and its twin outboard motors and glass fiber hull with inflatable sponsons make it an able craft. Self-righting is achieved by means of an air bag fitted on a frame over the stern. If the lifeboat should capsize, the air bag can be inflated from the upturned position, the stern is pushed up and the boat rights itself. Smaller lifeboats are also widely used and are ideal for rescue operations in shallow waters.

See also: Helicopter; Lifeboat.

Security system

There are two main aspects to modern security systems: protection against fire and against the theft of property or information. In some countries insuring the safety of individuals is also an important service. These functions are normally dealt with by firms that specialize in security, though where national interests are concerned they are dealt with by government agencies. Public services, such as the police and fire departments, deal with the same matters but with a different emphasis – in both cases a considerable part of the public effort has to be directed to active control measures, for example, firefighting or the detection and arrest of offenders.

Integrated systems

A great diversity of equipment is available for use in modern security systems, using a range of principles including ultrasonics, microwaves, infrared light, television, pressure and vibration sensors, heat sensors and other techniques. To make the best use of this equipment the designer of a comprehensive system to guard against fire and intruders must take into consideration where equipment will operate and how it will be operated, before selecting the methods to be used.

Invariably, alarm systems are designed to provide some audible or visible warning to security personnel, whether these are the police, firefighters or private security companies. Operators are, therefore, an important consideration in any security system, and most systems for stores, factories and buildings still rely on the store detective, watchman or patrolling guard. Where such systems are used, the security of the premises begins by insuring that the selection of the staff for such positions allows only people of the highest integrity to be appointed.

Various vetting, or screening, techniques are used to check the suitability of staff, including the thorough investigation of their background and the possible use of polygraphs (lie detector tests) coupled with psychological tests. Where appropriate, such tests are also carried out on other staff members, with different levels of screening being employed according to the degree of risk. The major security organizations provide uniformed guards who are fully trained and organized in either military or police manner. These companies also use guard dogs and have available armored vans for the transportation of money and valuables. Radio communication with headquarters is common and when on duty within premises the management usually extend to these guards the right to search and question staff.

The precise details of a security system will vary with the application but will often start with the

STORE AND OFFICE SECURITY SYSTEM

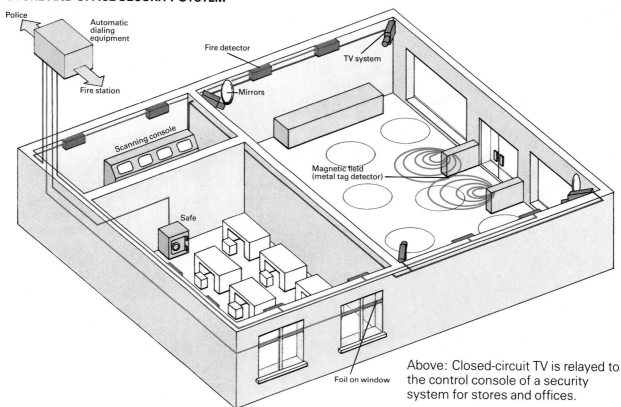

Above: Closed-circuit TV is relayed to the control console of a security system for stores and offices.

perimeter fences (or walls) which are designed to keep casual intruders out and may be fitted with sensors to warn of any attempts to gain entry. Area lighting aids surveillance, though increasing use of television systems with image intensifiers for low light levels and infrared detectors has reduced the need for area lighting. Entrance to a building, or to a secure area within a building, can be restricted to authorized personnel by means of password-operated entry systems and badge-reading systems with more sophisticated techniques like voice recognition being used where the highest security is required.

Devices, such as ultrasonic movement detectors and infrared beams (which give a signal when broken), allow the monitoring of movements, as do closed-circuit television systems with monitors in a security center. Such television systems can be coupled to other sensors so that the security guard's attention is immediately drawn to the appropriate screen if an intruder is suspected.

Recording systems allow a permanent record to be made of any events, although continuous recording of television signals is not common due to the very large amounts of tape required. One solution to this problem is to switch the recorders on only when the alarms have been activated. Another approach used in some bank systems is to record a series of still pictures, which may then be used for identification purposes with the definition being good enough to allow monitoring of the values of bills passed across the counter.

Regular patrols of the premises by security guards is another feature of most systems and the thoroughness of the patrol can be monitored by the use of checkpoints on the guard's beat. These checkpoints are fitted with equipment which has to be operated, using a key or password system, at specified times with a record being made for subsequent checking. More elaborate systems are connected to a central monitoring unit and provide an immediate alarm if a guard fails to check in at any point because he or she has been attacked.

Fire detection systems are normally linked in to the alarm system and once an intruder or fire has been detected the alarm is raised. In entirely automatic systems, the appropriate security services are alerted by automatic dialing systems, using the normal telephone service, special direct lines or radio links. In some cases the connection may be to the police or fire stations but frequently it is to a central station operated by the security firm, who then take the appropriate action, alerting their own mobile patrols as well as the police and fire services. Monitoring systems are used to check that the alarm circuits are working properly. They also help to reduce the number of false alarms, which waste the time of the police and fire departments and cause a noise nuisance.

Above: Beams of microwave are transmitted between two points of a fence. If anything crosses their path, an alarm nearby is triggered.

Store security

In stores, the use of television, mirrors and loop alarms are common in order to observe shoppers from a central area or to prevent the removal of display items. The experienced store detective, however, is still invaluable for observing the habits of potential shoplifters and for checking the honesty of the shop assistants. A common practice used by store detectives is a *test purchasing assignment*, which is carried out by two operatives working as a team. Both go to the same cash desk with items for purchase. Both note the cash register totals before and after the particular purchases and close attention is paid to all till procedures. If any suspicious procedure is observed, positive identification of the cashier and details of the event can be collated.

Equipment has also been designed which requires a metal tag to be attached to each saleable

Left: One of six closed-circuit TV cameras used for perimeter surveillance at an automobile assembly plant. Each camera is directly linked to a monitor in the central control room.
Above: Monitoring sections of this subway system with closed-circuit TV cameras enables constant checks to be made on the punctuality of trains.

item. When the customer pays for the goods the assistant removes the tag with a special tool. If the customer tries to take the goods from the shop with the tag remaining on the goods, equipment placed at the exits of the shop detects the tag through the disturbance of a magnetic field. In another design, the tag returns high-frequency radio signals to a transmitter–receiver system at the exit, so triggering the alarm.

Fire protection

Fire affects not only property, but more importantly life. Fire systems must, therefore, not only give an early warning of an outbreak of fire but also provide some means of dousing the fire and preventing it from advancing into other areas. Fire alarm systems operate by splitting the protected area into zones and continuously monitoring each zone. The first signs of combustion, which normally produces invisible particles, can be detected by IONIZATION detectors, in which there is a small radioactive source. The minute particles present enter the detector and alter the normal current passing through the detection chamber, immediately setting off the alarm.

As the combustion increases and smoke appears, it can be detected by equipment which uses photoelectric cells and a light source. The smoke entering the unit reduces the light intensity at the photoelectric cell and an alarm is created. When flames finally occur their presence can be detected by infra-

red detectors. Usually circuitry in the units also detects the flicker rate of flames to prevent false alarms from normal infrared sources, such as heaters. Changes in temperature can also be detected with *bimetallic strips*, made of two metals which have different expansion characteristics. At a predetermined temperature the different expansion rates cause the strip to bend far enough to open and produce alarm conditions.

Control panels can be designed so that the operation of any alarm in a zone can be made to trigger an automatic extinguishing system which can use water, or gas where computer or other electric equipment is housed. Smoke doors can be automatically closed, and fuel supply valves closed.

New security risks

With new advances in technology the problems of security increase. Along with their many advantages to business, computers have brought the problem that all the information relating to the business can be stolen, altered or easily copied by anyone who has access to the computer room. Conventional security techniques are used to restrict access to the computer area with password and key systems being further used to control and identify the actual computer operators and users. Similarly, remote terminals have to be closely supervised, and checks made to insure that the communications lines have not been tapped. Various forms of encryption (coding) are often now used to protect data.

Right: Electronic locks installed on the outer doors of this bank allow customers access to the cash-dispensing machines inside when the bank is unstaffed. The lock reads information stored magnetically on the back of the cards and admits only those with valid cards, effectively excluding all but the bank's own customers from the bank. Once inside, the same card is used to obtain cash from the automatic dispensing machines.

• FACT FILE •

- A recently developed countermeasure against cat burglars is an anticlimb paint for drainpipes. It is greasy and nondrying, and contains a chemical that is difficult to remove completely from the skin.

- Scientists are working on a miniature transmitter that can be surgically implanted close to the collarbone of people, such as diplomats who risk being kidnapped. Monitors tuned to the transmitter can trace the victim even before the kidnappers have made their demands.

- One intruder sensor available for security systems consists of a gold-plated metal ball supported by sharp metal points. The slightest vibration breaks the alarm circuit, but the alarm is delayed until an analyzer has identified the intruder.

- In an automobile specially built for the late Shah of Iran, sudden treachery from a passenger could be dealt with spectacularly by means of concealed shotgun beneath the passenger seat.

Security programs also prevent unauthorized use of secure data files, and the main operating software should be interlocked to prevent tampering. A skilled programer can overcome most such security arrangements, as shown by the success of *hackers* in breaking into computer systems. Further protection may be provided by storing sensitive data on removable media (disks and tapes) which are held in secure storage when not in use. With all systems, though, security depends to a large extent on the personal integrity of the programers and operators.

Invasion of privacy

Most effective security systems rely on large numbers of personnel, the use of whom creates problems, not merely by physically interfering with people's freedom of movement, but also because the public feels threatened by what virtually amounts to a private army of security people. Any increase in security inevitably interferes with individual freedom, and makes demands on people's willingness to be questioned and searched.

Reinforcement of security precautions is invariably claimed to be in the public's best interests. Some doubt is thrown on this claim, however, by the increasingly violent methods used by security guards, and by criminals to overcome these increasingly thorough precautions. In this sort of mutual escalation the public loses on all counts.

See also: Burglar alarm; Lock, security.

Seeing aid

Vision may account for as much as 95 per cent of all the information that reaches the human brain from the sense organs. When eyes, ears or the hands pick up information, trains of nerve impulses travel at speed to that part of the brain that handles each kind of sensory input, and it is here that vision scores because the nerve fibers from the retina to the visual cortex are numbered in millions. When reading print, whole word outlines are transmitted via these fibers to give comprehension rates about twice as high as the speed at which ordinary speech can be understood.

Losing this rapid and convenient information source is obviously a great problem to a blind or partially sighted person. There are, however, many devices available to those with impaired eyesight that can help with a surprising range of everyday activities. Some aids are simple adaptations of everyday objects – for example, clocks and watches with hinged glasses so that the blind person can tell the time by touching the hands – and others use high technology in novel ways.

In Britain the pioneering researches of Lord Fraser of Lonsdale (1897–1974) made a significant contribution toward reducing some of the main handicaps of blindness. The first talking book on LP records in the 1930s and the development of an 18-track magnetic tape cassette in the years immediately after World War II led to the British Talking Book Service which soon became very popular. Personal reading and mobility aids also featured prominently in his research programs at St Dunstan's, London, and the multidisciplinary approach adopted has encouraged researchers in several other countries to support similar investigations to help the disabled.

The Braille system

Braille, a tactile reading system, was invented by a Frenchman, Louis Braille (1809–52), a blind teacher at the Institution Nationale des Jeunes Aveugles, Paris, France. Braille is an alphabet composed of various combinations of one to six raised dots, which can be in various positions on a six-dot oblong area – the *Braille cell*. There are no less than 63 ways in which these dots may be arranged in the cell. The full complement, that is two dots on each of the three lines, each pair placed vertically one above the other, represents the word *for*; a single dot in the top line, left hand side, is *a*. Codes of dots also exist for specialized subjects such as mathematics and music. It is now possible to have automatic translation into Braille using computer techniques.

An industry has sprung up around Braille, with a large range of products available to write in Braille,

Above: The Optacon reading device includes a hand-held miniature camera which scans a line while the index finger of the other hand rests on the tactile screen. Vibrating reeds form the letter shape against the finger. Reading rates of between 30 and 50 wpm can be achieved on this machine.

from typewriters and shorthand machines to *styles* – pointed writing tools – and writing frames, to help position the dots correctly and to assist letter spacing. There are many books published in Braille, but they are very expensive to produce.

Reading aid

There are two main kinds of reading aid in use – those that produce audible tones, and those that produce tactile patterns. The aural reading aids date back to 1912, when the Optophone was designed. The typewriter-sized device has six PHOTO-CELLS which are scanned across printed material. The result is a series of tones or chords in the reader's earphones which relate to the occurrence of black ink beneath the photocells. The Optophone is not an efficient way of reading because, even after a year's training, the average rate of reading is only five words per minute (wpm).

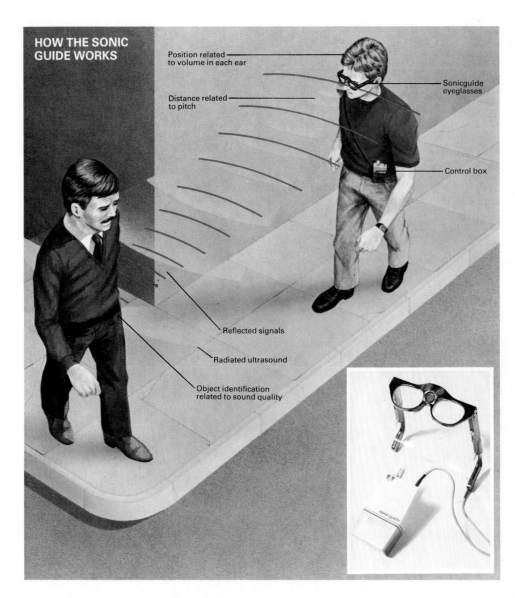

HOW THE SONIC GUIDE WORKS

Position related to volume in each ear

Distance related to pitch

Sonicguide eyeglasses

Control box

Reflected signals

Radiated ultrasound

Object identification related to sound quality

Left: The Sonicguide gives the blind user a new awareness of the environment. A transmitter located in the bridge of the glasses broadcasts high-frequency sound signals, which are reflected by objects in the vicinity, to be picked up by microphones which are also housed in the glasses. The reflected ultrasound is then converted into stereophonic signals. The pitch of the sound, heard via earphones in the arms of the glasses, gives the distances of objects; quality of pitch indicates texture; volume denotes position. The small box holds the controls.

The Stereotoner is another reading aid based on Optophone principles of converting print into musical tones. There are nine photocells in the sensing head and the musical output is shared between the ears. The *descenders* (strokes below the line) are fed to the left ear, and the tones resulting from the on line and ascending strokes are heard in the right ear in an attempt to improve reading rates. The Stereotoner is an example of miniaturization: built-in rechargeable nickel-cadmium batteries provide energy for the photodetectors, driving the nine tuned oscillators and a light source to give uniform illumination of the print.

The instrument is tracked manually across the page and maintained on line with the aid of a guide strip laid across the page. A small gifted group of users in the U.S. read personal mail and check documents with this reading aid.

The Optocon – from optical to tactile conversion of print – uses a camera to scan lines of print. A grid of photodiodes detects the shape of the letter, which is relayed to a corresponding grid of 144 rods. The index finger is positioned over the grid and detects vertical movements of the rods. Reading rates of between 30 and 50 wpm can be routinely achieved. Alternate lens modules permit the reading of computer visual display units, pocket calculators and typescript, providing a valuable occupational aid.

Some researchers are looking toward computer technology for a truly useful reading aid. OPTICAL CHARACTER RECOGNITION (OCR) systems are being perfected to enable computers to read. Kurzweil computer products have been making a reading machine which converts printed text to speech form since the mid-1970s. The latest model couples artificial intelligence to OCR; text scanned is translated into speech by a synthesized speech module. Even more sophisticated devices are planned.

Above: Using the Diplograph, Braille and normal alphabet could be written simultaneously. One disc bore Braille and the corresponding letters on its face, but only Braille on its writing edge, whereas the other disc had inked printing type.

Below: In the Optacon reading machine, light from a page falling on the phototransistor array is converted into electronic impulses which activate the piezoelectric dimorphs, vibrating reeds which recreate the shape of the letters on a tactile or touch-sensitive display unit.

Mobility aid

In 1960, the Englishman L. Kay began researches at Britain's University of Birmingham into the usefulness of a small flashlight-like echo location mobility aid. One very helpful device of this type, the Mark II Binaural Sensory aid, is built into eye-glass frames. It uses frequency-modulated (FM) ultrasonic waves sent out from a transmitter built into the bridge alongside two microphones.

In operation a beam of sound waves 60 degrees wide probes the space ahead for a distance of about 10 ft (3 m) and detected obstacles or guide surfaces, such as buildings, bounce echoes back to be picked up by the aid's twin receivers. The FM waves have a frequency of 90 kHz, pulsing four times per second, and slight differences in the beat frequency of returned echoes from obstacles are electronically converted and heard as audio tones in twin ear pieces. The tones are directly related to the distance of the reflecting object in the path, and the traveler learns eventually to relate pitch to the distance of a hazard ahead.

The aid is used in conjunction with a long cane because the beam of sound waves is only 30 degrees in elevation, that is, from waist to head height, and so hazards at ground level are not detected, but a traveler's awareness of the near environment is still heightened by a significant amount.

PRINCIPLE OF THE OPTACON READING MACHINE

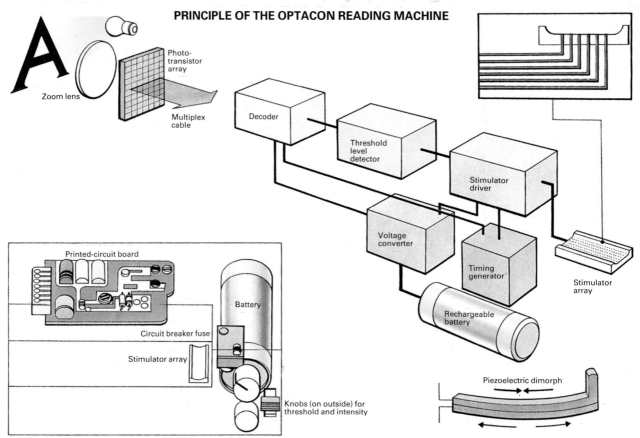

Thousands of blind people use the long cane to aid their mobility as an alternative to the guide dog. The cane, which is about 40 per cent longer than an ordinary walking stick, is scanned from side to side, the tip contacting the ground one pace ahead.

Researchers in the U.S. have incorporated three laser beams into a modified long cane. The lasers, mounted near the crook handle, direct their beams in three well-defined elevations: below ground level to detect sudden drop-offs, in the main direction three or four paces ahead, and above for head–height obstacles. At about 1.5 ft (0.5 m) down the cane, three photodetecting diodes gather information about any hazards, which reflect the laser probing beam back to the cane. Sudden drops in the terrain are signaled by a low audio tone from an amplifier at the end of the crook handle, high tones indicate head-high overhanging obstacles, while the ahead beam gives warning by vibrating a small stud on which the index finger rests when using the cane.

The laser's pencil-thin beams are given width by virtue of the lateral scanning action of the cane, which picks up information about terrain level one pace ahead.

All these kinds of mobility aids may become outdated if the predictions of some farsighted workers in the field of robotics come true. The day may come when electronic guide dogs which need no lengthy training schedule replace the now familiar animals.

Industrial aid

The Braille MICROMETER caliper is a highly successful adaptation of the most widely used measuring instrument for precision engineering components. The usual visual scales are replaced by embossed calibrations and Braille numerals on two integrally geared drums. When a component is checked between the anvils in the caliper, the measurment is read by touch against an embossed datum line on the non-rotatable center drum. The pinion-to-gear ratio between the drums is 40:1, and there are 25 and 40 divisions respectively to give a 0.001 in. (0.025 mm) resolution. Four decimal place resolution is provided on a five-division VERNIER scale adjacent to the datum line.

The usual micrometer screw thread pitch is retained to advance or retract the measuring drum assembly when checking a component. This adaptation has been made to micrometers measuring up to 6 in. (152 mm) and to depth gauges and, with appropriate calibrations, to high-resolution bevel protractors. Developments such as these have enabled blind people to do types of work previously open only to sighted people.

See also: Audio-visual; Character recognition; Eye; Frequency modulation; Laser and maser; Photoelectric cell; Voice analysis.

Below: This speech synthesizer converts binary digital readouts of electronic measuring systems into sound, enabling blind people to work alongside sighted people in industry.

Below: The Kurzweil reading machine translates printed text into speech. The text is scanned by an optical character recognition device, then read out by means of a synthesized speech module.

Seismology

Seismology means the study of earthquakes. Because humans first lived in earthquake-prone areas such as Ethiopia, Mesopotamia and Indonesia, they have always known and feared earthquakes. In the past century, however, they have turned them into a powerful tool for investigating the Earth's interior. Now it seems possible that we may soon be able to control earthquakes to some extent.

In AD 132 a device for registering seismic activity was made by Chang Hêng, in China. It had a number of metal balls around the rim of an urn, arranged so that an earth tremor would disturb a central column, operating a mechanism which dropped one of the balls into a metal holder causing a noise. The direction of the earthquake could be worked out by seeing which balls fell and which did not. From this primitive device today's sensitive *seismometers* evolved, and a science has grown up with them. There is now an industry involved in using artificially generated seismic shocks to search the Earth's crust for minerals. Despite the small scale of its operations it has so far provided a wealth of knowledge on conditions near the Earth's surface.

Seismographs

In the past hundred years there have been many advances in the design of the seismographs which record the movements of the Earth's crust at their location. There is now seismic recording equipment fixed in every country, making continuous recordings. There is also portable equipment which can be installed for temporary projects. Any device which measures seismic activity is a seismometer; those which record the activity, for example, by means of a pen recorder, are known as seismographs.

It has not proved possible to design a seismograph to measure faithfully the movement of the Earth's crust in every direction at once in response to seismic waves. What invariably happens is that each seismic observatory has at least two seismographs, one each for the horizontal and vertical parts of the movement. Often there are three – the horizontal component is measured in two directions.

The horizontal component seismograph consists of a pendulum with a heavy weight. Just as Léon Foucault's pendulum, which is extremely long, always swings in the same direction in space, so showing up the rotation of the Earth beneath it, the seismograph pendulum tends to stay in the same place by virtue of its INERTIA while the ground vibrates beneath it. The difference is that the seismograph pendulum is not set swinging – it is restrained from swinging by means of *damping* of some kind. The pendulum has a resonant period – the time it would normally take to complete a whole

Above: A volcano erupts at El Chicon, Mexico. Seismological studies of earthquake waves have shown that the lava flowing from volcanoes comes from isolated pockets of molten material within the mainly solid outer 1400 miles of the Earth.

swing – and if the period of the earthquake waves happens to coincide with this the result will be meaningless. Periods expected from seismic activity are approximately 1/100 to 3000 seconds, and one seismograph will not be suitable for the entire range. Consequently, a range of seismographs is needed, including some with a long resonant period to measure the longer-period waves. A true pendulum with a period of many seconds would be impractical, so a practical pendulum seismograph consists of a weight on a horizontal beam, pivoted at the end, suspended by a wire from a point not quite above the pivot. The pendulum is slightly out of balance, and if pushed will swing with a period of up to a minute.

The vertical component seismograph is essentially a weight on the end of a spring. As in the case of the horizontal component device, the period of vibration of the spring is increased by holding the weight out at a slight angle by means of a horizontal bar. The ground movement is measured by the extension of the spring. The exact value of the disturbance, typically less than 0.04 in. (1 mm), can only be found if the physical characteristics of the seismograph are available.

More recent seismographs use electromagnetism. They are made of electrically inductive material and are surrounded by coils, so that an electric current is produced when the pendulum moves. The damping is also carried out electromagnetically. This is a very sensitive arrangement and also gives a tape output which can be readily used with computers so that the information can be analyzed.

A specialized type of seismograph, first introduced in 1935, allows the strain in the Earth's materials to be measured directly. This is useful in earthquake areas, and works by recording the variation in distance between two points some 60 ft (18 m) apart. Also revealing close to the epicenters of quakes are tiltmeters which show the build-up in tilt before large earthquakes.

Earth studies

Waves from earthquakes and, lately, artificial explosions can reveal a great deal about the Earth's interior.The waves generated are of three main types. The first are *surface waves*, which are very

Below: Deep-focus quakes have little effect at the surface, but their location can be discovered by comparing the records from different stations.

strong close to the earthquake's epicenter where they cause most of the damage due to the quake. These waves are attenuated (reduced in intensity) rapidly, however, and become undetectable in most cases about 200 miles (320 km) from the epicenter, though there are some much weaker *love waves* which can travel great distances. But at a distance from the epicenter the waves observed are generally those which have traveled through the body of the Earth itself. These are normally called *P-waves* and *S-waves*, being primary and secondary respectively. They can also be thought of as P-waves being push-pull and S-waves being shake. These differ because in P-waves the particles of the material through which the wave passes are moved backward and forward along the line of travel, and in S-waves the movement is perpendicular to the line of travel. It is a rule that P-waves travel faster than S-waves, which is why they arrive at an observing station sooner and are therefore called primary. In addition, S-waves are attenuated so heavily by liquids that they will effectively not pass through liquids at all. Every major property change inside the Earth, such as the division between the crust (the outermost layer) and mantle (the bulk of the Earth), acts as a source of P- and S-waves as a result of every wave which meets it, so that the various layers of the Earth are distinguishable by the waves from their upper and lower surfaces. In addition, the outer part of the Earth's central core is known to

SEISMOGRAPH RECORDS OF AN EARTHQUAKE

P = primary waves
S = secondary waves
L = love waves

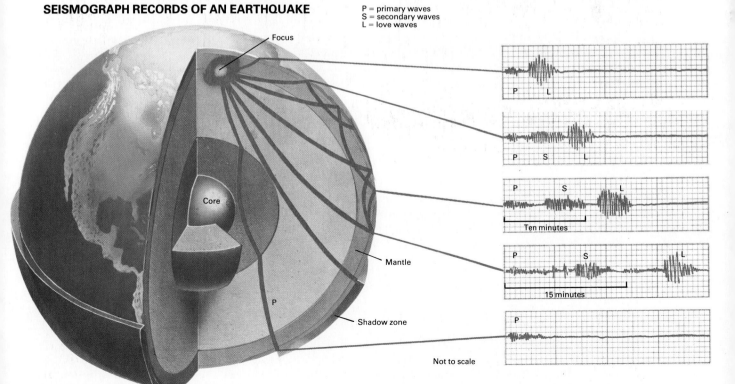

Focus

Core

Mantle

Shadow zone

P

Ten minutes

15 minutes

Not to scale

Left: This sophisticated apparatus to monitor changes in the Earth's crust, the tilt of the landscape, and even such things as the Earth's gravity and magnetism, has been set up in Tokyo, an area prone to earthquakes. In densely populated urban areas, advance warnings of quakes would prevent the loss of thousands of lives. Below: Studying a trace of the North Sea made by setting off a series of arc discharges underwater and then detecting the echoes from the rocks.

be liquid because it does not transmit S-waves.

In the late nineteenth century it was observed that earthquake waves, apart from surface waves, received very close to the epicenter (the point on the surface vertically above the earthquake center, or focus) are heavily attenuated and altered or completely lost, causing an apparent shadow. Other shadow zones are observed at different distances from the epicenter, and during the early years of this century this fact was used to discover the nature of the various interior layers of the Earth. The core, for example, was discovered in 1906 as a result of a shadow zone on the far side of the Earth from the epicenter in which few waves are received. It almost certainly consists of liquid iron and nickel, firstly because these are major constituents of metallic meteorites, from which the planets are believed to have accumulated, and also because the pressure and temperatures which must exist there would not allow any other likely liquid to exist.

The IDA network

In the early 1980s the International Deployment of Accelerometers (IDA) Seismic Network was set up. The IDA network is an array of specially designed ultralong-period seismographs arranged around the Earth, dividing the crust into 20 equal-area triangles. The aim of the IDA Network is to study *Earth tides* – distortions of the Earth's crust caused by the interaction of the Earth's and the Moon's gravitational fields – and the Earth's *normal modes*. In the period following a large earthquake the whole planet is set into oscillation, like a bell. The oscillations, which occur at a discrete set of resonant frequencies, are the normal modes. The longest

period mode is 54 minutes; the shortest 30 seconds.

The sensors (La Coste and Romberg gravity meters) have detection periods longer than 20 seconds. Employing a *zero-length spring* – corresponding to a regular pendulum with an extremely long period – they have a low mechanical drift, allowing the minute movements of the crust to be measured accurately.

Earthquake prediction

Earthquakes are caused by some adjustment of the Earth's material, and may be deep or shallow. The shallow earthquakes, within 30 miles (50 km) of the

EARTHQUAKE WAVES

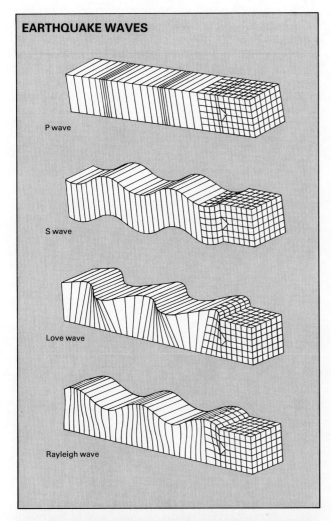

P wave

S wave

Love wave

Rayleigh wave

Left: Earthquake waves travel in different modes and at different velocities through the Earth. The intervals between the arrival of each type of wave at a seismic station can tell scientists where a quake occurred, and how strong it was.

Earth's surface, are by far the most numerous, and mainly occur in zones of geological activity such as the midocean ridges, edges of continents, and large volcanic areas such as Hawaii. They are caused by friction in bodies of magma – molten material – welling up to the surface at the centers of oceans or by material moving back down into the Earth at the edges of continents. As the magma makes its way to the surface, it must alter its chemical form many times. These *changes of state* involve changes in crystal structure and hence in volume. This always results in expansion, because the temperature and pressure of the material are falling steadily. This forces surrounding rocks to move aside, and the disturbance sends the waves through the Earth.

Heat is also released by the changes in state undergone by the minerals, and these help to drive the volcanic activity in the midocean ridges, resulting in increased heat flow along these ridges and their landward extensions such as the central part of Iceland and the rift valley of Ethiopia.

At the edges of the oceans (in cases where material is moving downward) the situation is almost exactly the opposite. Material is carried (by the same convection currents that cause the upwelling) deep into the Earth's crust where it remelts, and, as it goes, corresponding changes of state occur. Hence at the edges of oceans the deeper earthquakes occur away from the ocean and close to the nearby continental land mass. Here, too, volcanoes are driven by the accompanying heat, so that island chains such as Japan are built of volcanic material. The earthquakes to the southeast of Japan, in the deep ocean trench where the material sinks, are only a few miles down, while those below Tokyo are many tens of miles down.

Earthquakes are measured on scales of intensity, one of them being that of Mercalli, which goes from 1 to 12. The lower figures measure mild quakes and the larger increasingly catastrophic ones. However, the Mercalli scale lacks scientific precision and the Richter scale is often used instead, particularly for measuring severe earthquakes which on the Mercalli scale would all be classified at 12. The intensity measured may be quoted either as its strength at the observing station, or as the intensity which it would have had at the epicenter. Many earthquakes take place in remote regions where there are no seismographs to record them, but their strengths are known from the records at distant stations.

See also: Earth; Earthquake; Plate tectonics.

• FACT FILE •

- At a depth of 3700 miles (6000 km) the pressure of the Earth's core, measured by changes in seismic wave velocity, is 3.5 million times as high as the atmospheric pressure at the Earth's surface.

- 435 miles (700 km) is the greatest depth at which earthquakes have been detected by seismologists. At this depth descending slabs of the Earth's mantle become a part of the surrounding material.

- In order to reproduce deep mantle and core pressures in the laboratory seismologists use the diamond-anvil cell in which materials are compressed between the sharp points of diamonds, giving enormous pressures over small areas.

Semaphore machine

A semaphore machine is a type of mechanical telegraph or signaling machine in which movable arms on a central post follow a table of signs to spell out a message. This can be relayed over long distances in clear weather by a chain of stations on high points of land, each within sight of the next. Also, a man using his arms and holding flags to make him more readily visible can communicate by the semaphore signs with anyone who has a clear view of him.

The brothers Ignace and Claude Chappe developed a line of semaphore stations between Paris and Lille in 1794 for passing official information. Their system was based on a beam about 12 ft (4 m) long with pivoted arms or extensions at both ends. This beam was itself centrally pivoted at the top of a mast and by means of ropes, pulleys and counterweights could indicate 36 different signs. There was a crew of three; one person with a telescope announced the signs from the sending station and observed that the next station was repeating them correctly, the second operated the winches to make the signs and the third wrote down the message and told the second person what to send. Each sign took 20 seconds: 4 seconds to make and 16 seconds to allow it to be read and understood.

A contemporary British system was the *shutter telegraph*, established by the Admiralty in 1795. This used six separately controlled discs on a frame, pivoted at their center so that any or all of them could be turned to a horizontal position, making

Right: Thirty-six codes were used for the semaphore machine developed by the Frenchmen Ignace and Claude Chappe. Messages were sent by a team of three. Each sign took about 20 seconds to send, so transmitting lengthy messages over a long distance – for example, via a series of towers between Paris and Lille – could be a time-consuming process.
Far right: A sectional view of a mechanical telegraph tower. It was based on a beam 12 ft (4 m) long with pivoted arms at both ends, which were operated by means of ropes, pulleys, and counterweights.

THE 36 SIGNS OF CHAPPE'S SEMAPHORE SYSTEM

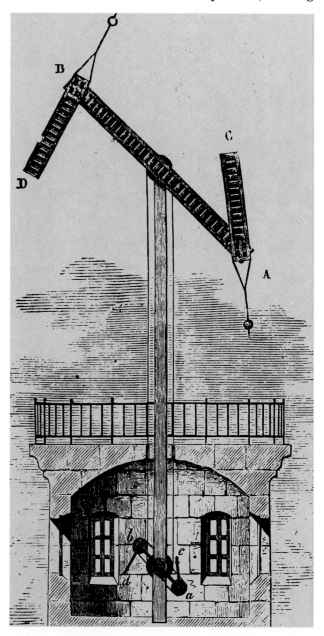

them invisible at a distance. It was not, strictly speaking, a semaphore, since it had no arms. It was less clear than the French semaphore; British officers recognized this and developed their own versions of the French invention. In 1808 Sir Charles W. Pasley designed a semaphore with two arms pivoted at the top of a post. Sir Home Popham put forward at the same date his idea of two pivoted arms, one lower than the other on the post; this the Admiralty adopted. He also proposed a form for use

Below: The semaphore machine designed by Englishman Sir Home Popham had two arms controlled by gears and rods. A separate display showed the operator the arm positions on dials.

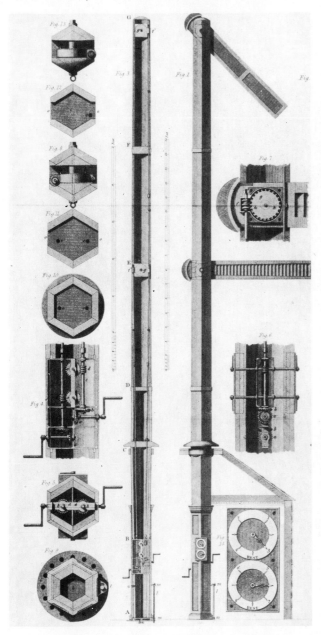

in ships, which had two posts each with one arm, and this was introduced into the Fleet in 1816.

The Admiralty shutter stations were closed after the end of the Napoleonic War and new sites chosen for semaphore stations. A line from Chatham, near London, was opened in 1816 and one to Portsmouth in 1822. From this a branch line to Plymouth was begun, but abandoned in 1831. In 1822 Pasley's single post semaphore was used in ships, since it was more distinct than Popham's two-post type.

Semaphore houses, some of several stories according to the height of the ground, were built on the selected sites. A hollow hexagonal mast, 30 ft (9 m) high above the roof, sprang from the operating room. Here the crew, a lieutenant and his assistant, were equipped with telescopes and controlled a pair of cranks which operated the two arms, 8 ft (2.5 m) long and 1 ft 4 in. (0.5 m) wide. These arms were housed inside the mast when not in use. Henry Maudslay, inventor of the screw-cutting lathe, manufactured the gearing and chains, and later rods, which operated the arms. Two pairs of dials indicated to the operator the true reading of the arms from whichever side the mast was viewed. There were 48 possible signs, allowing for alphabetical and numerical sequences as well as signs with special significance. Rate of sending was about five words a minute.

A time signal was passed daily from the Royal Obsevatory, Greenwich, to Whitehall in London and on down the Portsmouth line; this was a distance of 68 miles (109 km), and went through 15 stations in a time of 45 seconds. The last message on this line was sent on December 31, 1847. The advent of the electric telegraph had rendered the semaphore stations obsolete. One or two of the buildings remain today and many points of high land on maps, marked Telegraph Hill, are in fact semaphore sites.

Use of the system by the Navy and Army continued. Small semaphore machines were used in ships, on the signal bridge, up to World War II. A *truck semaphore* (a masthead type) was also introduced about 1890. In this steel wire ropes, adjustable in length by bottle screws, connected the operating handles on the bridge to the arms at the top of the mast. Frequent adjustment was required.

Naval signal ratings were required to be proficient in sending and reading semaphore messages by hand flags at the rate of 15 to 20 words a minute. From ship to ship or from ship to shore, operators could converse freely, even without using flags. Today, semaphore signaling is not taught and MORSE CODE sent by wire is used instead.

Railway signals worked mechanically are also called semaphore, but they are scarcely used.

See also: Gear; Pulley; Telegraph; Telescope.

Semiconductor

Materials can be divided into three main types according to the way in which they allow the flow of electricity when a *potential difference* (voltage) is applied across them. With *insulators* there is no current flow, while with *conductors* a comparatively large current flow will occur, the magnitude of the flow (for a given potential difference) depending on the *conductance* of the material. The third type of material is the *semiconductor* which, as the name suggests, has properties that lie between those of conductors and insulators with a limited current flow occurring. The conductivity of a semiconductor varies considerably with the purity of the material and with external factors such as temperature and incident light, and the control of such variables allows a range of electronic devices to be produced.

A large number of chemical elements and com-pounds have semiconductor properties with the most important being germanium and silicon (group IV), and the III–V compounds formed from elements such as gallium, arsenic, indium and phosphorus (the numerals refer to groups in the PERIODIC TABLE). In these materials the electric conductivity is determined by the number of elementary positive charges (*holes*) and negative charges (*electrons*) which are free to move and so can take part in conduction. The density of these *free carriers*, and hence the conductivity, depend on the material structure, the presence of certain impurities and the temperature.

Although the concept of a positive charge carrier – a hole – is difficult to explain rigorously, being based on QUANTUM MECHANICS, it can be considered as simply being an electron vacancy (that is the absence of an electron from a *valency bond* of the semiconductor crystal). For example, silicon is a tetravalent compound with each of the four electrons in the outer shell being shared by the four neighboring atoms to give four COVALENT BONDS. With a pure, defect-free crystal at low (*absolute*) temperatures these bonds are intact but as the temperature rises some of the bonds will be broken, releasing electrons and creating holes.

The electrons can move through the crystal, as in

Below: Impurities in the lattice produce an excess or lack of electrons. Mobile electrons drift through the material. Holes, however, are stationary, but resemble positive flow of charge. These properties are used for the PNP transistor junction shown here with a low forward bias.

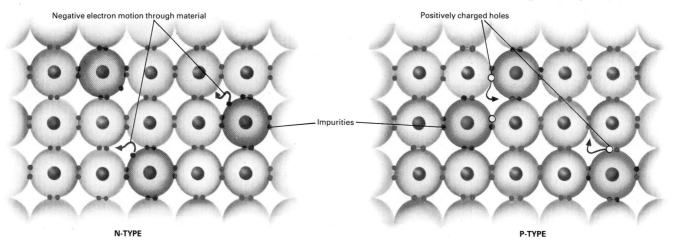

N-TYPE

P-TYPE

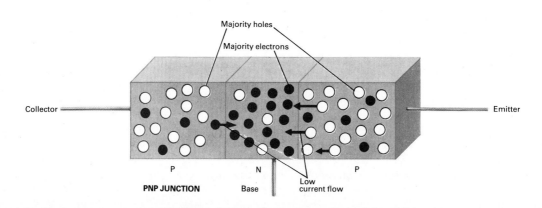

PNP JUNCTION

Above: Pure silicon wafers in a quartz tube prior to diffusion, which involves melting a wafer with the right amount of dopant and cooling it to form a single crystal with the right orientation.

a conductor, and so can the holes. This movement is achieved by the transfer of an electron from some other area to fill the original hole, while creating a hole at its original position. In a pure semiconductor the number of holes produced is equal to the number of electrons and such a material is also known as an *intrinsic* semiconductor. When a potential difference is applied across the semiconductor the electrons move toward the positive potential and the holes toward the negative potential, and the total current flow is the sum of the electron and hole currents.

The number and type of the charge carriers in an *extrinsic* semiconductor are controlled by the addition of *doping* impurities with the number of valence electrons of the impurity determining the type of carrier produced. With impurites such as phosphorus and arsenic, which have five valence electrons, four of the electrons can bond normally to the tetravalent silicon crystal structure, leaving a free electron. The effect is to increase the number of free electrons, giving an *n-type* (n for negative) semiconductor with a preponderance of free electrons. In contrast doping with boron, which is trivalent, results in an excess of holes and gives a *p-type* (p for positive) semiconductor. Free electrons still exist in p-type semiconductors and are known as *minority carriers*, as are free holes in n-type semiconductors, while the holes (or electrons in n-type semiconductors) are known as *majority carriers*.

A p-n semiconductor junction is produced when there is a change from one type of impurity to the other within the same crystal structure. Semiconductor devices such as diodes and transistors are based on the use of such junctions to give specific current flow characteristics.

Development

Semiconductors have been in use for many years, their first application being in the fabrication of metal RECTIFIERS. These devices used semiconducting copper oxide or selenium, which formed a rectifying contact with a metal electrode. Later, germanium was used with a point contact consisting of a thin metal whisker. This device also acts as a rectifier, but at a much lower current level.

The real growth in semiconductor technology came with the development of the *junction transistor*, which consists of two adjacent p-n junctions in a p-n-p or an n-p-n arrangement with three connecting electrodes. Subsequent development resulted in a number of other transistor arrangements and INTEGRATED CIRCUITS containing large numbers of interconnected components. The material used for most semiconductor devices is silicon, which has to be produced to a high standard of purity.

Applications

Although the greatest usage of semiconductors is in the manufacture of silicon transistors and integrated circuits, many other devices and materials are of very great commercial importance.

The dependence of a semiconductor's electric properties on illumination by light or by other forms of radiation has led to the development of a wide range of PHOTOSENSORS. Different materials have sensitivity in different parts of the wavelength spectrum, extending out to the infrared region. A similar application is that of power generation by the solar cell, vital to spacecraft but of potential use on Earth as well.

Semiconductors can also generate light. Indicators and displays are now available in many colors, using the Light Emitting Diode (LED) in which current through a p-n junction of relatively complex semiconducting compounds causes radiation of a color which is characteristic of the material. Coherent light can also be produced by semiconductor lasers for use in fiber optic communications systems.

Semiconductor elements are now widely used in strain and pressure TRANSDUCERS, enabling the measurement device to be fully integrated with a sensitive amplifier, with a consequent improvement in performance. It is clear that we have not yet seen all the potential value of semiconductors. There are probably other material properties to be discovered and exploited, such as the high-frequency oscillations of the GUNN EFFECT in gallium arsenide, which are used for microwave oscillators.

See also: Conduction; Electricity; Electron; Integrated circuit; Silicon chip; Transducer.

Sensory science

Humans have a very poor sense of smell compared with other animals. Silk moths can attract mates by smell when several miles apart and a salmon can smell its way thousands of miles back to its birthplace – feats inconceivable for humans with their limited nasal powers. So, while for animals the chemical senses of olfaction (smell) and gustation (taste) are the most important sources for gaining information about their surroundings, this is not the case for humans, for whom sight, hearing and touch are more important. Indeed, in animals the olfactory and gustatory senses probably developed far earlier than the more technically sophisticated senses of sight and hearing; even primitive species have well-developed smell and taste capabilities.

Communicating messages

Among higher animals, the sense of smell and its counterpart, the chemical communication of messages between individuals, are used for an astonishing variety of purposes. These include territorial, social and sexual behavior and defense or escape from predators, as well as the more obvious applications of food location and selection and the avoidance of poisonous substances.

A chemical sense is found throughout the animal kingdom, although it is only among the *vertebrates* (fish, amphibians, reptiles, birds and mammals) that smell and taste are distinguished through the existence of separate receptors, nerve pathways and brain centers for olfaction and gustation. At the lowest level of animal life, single-celled organisms such as amoebae can detect chemical substances that impinge upon their surface membranes, and as a result can direct themselves through chemical gradients toward higher concentrations of substances they need to maintain life, or away from noxious substances.

Seawater provides an ideal medium for a chemical sense, and the simplest animals to have specialized olfactory cells are the marine-living *coelenterates* – sea-anemones, jellyfish and hydra. Crustaceans such as prawns and lobsters use highly sensitive receptors in the hairs attached to their antennules and legs to detect amino acid concentrations as low as one part in a million, and in this way are led to decaying animals and plants that form a large part of their diet.

Nearly all vertebrate species possess a distinct olfactory organ consisting of an area of tissue packed with nerve cells specially adapted to the detection of chemical substances. Usually the cells bear several hairs or *cilia* (hairlike vibrating

Left: A fly lured by its senses to the mouth of the pitcher trap of a Sarracenia plant, where it is in danger of losing its life. Insects are attracted by a bright red color inside the pitcher, or by a viscous sugary fluid secreted near its entrance. The insects fall into a digestive fluid and are unable to get a foothold in the long, downward-pointing hairs of the plant, so they drown.

HOW THE HUMAN NOSE AND BRAIN CONNECT

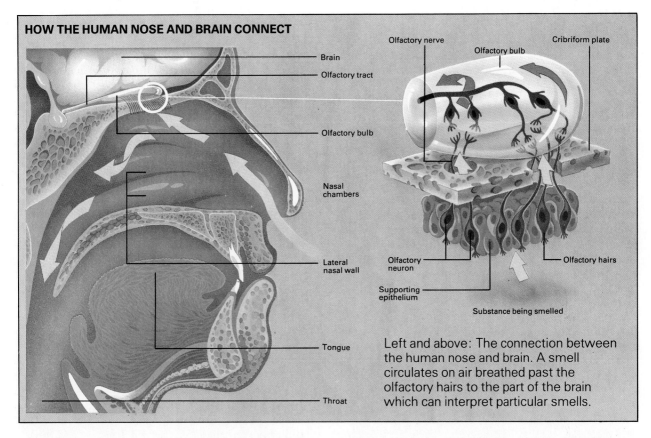

Brain
Olfactory tract
Olfactory bulb
Nasal chambers
Lateral nasal wall
Tongue
Throat

Olfactory nerve
Olfactory bulb
Cribriform plate
Olfactory hairs
Olfactory neuron
Supporting epithelium
Substance being smelled

Left and above: The connection between the human nose and brain. A smell circulates on air breathed past the olfactory hairs to the part of the brain which can interpret particular smells.

organs), the surfaces of which are thought to contain receptor sites for odorous substances. The cells are all connected by means of long nerve *axons* – filaments carrying nerve cells – to two protuberances from the brain called the olfactory bulbs.

In reptiles, birds and mammals, the olfactory organ is situated within the animal's respiratory tract, so that olfaction is an inevitable accompaniment to breathing. In fish, however, the organ is separate from the gills and consists of a chamber through which water is forced to pass because of the fish's motion through the water.

Many terrestrial vertebrates also possess an additional olfactory organ, called Jacobson's organ, situated in a pouch leading off from the respiratory tract at the back of the mouth. In snakes and other reptiles this organ detects odors that waft up from substances that are picked up by the tongue.

The territorial behavior of many species depends on each member of the species staking out an area by urinating around its perimeter; other members of the species are then warned off by the odor given off by the urine. Some migratory animals such as salmon depend almost exclusively on olfaction to find their way from place to place. Within groups of animals, different individuals may recognize each other by their different odors, and chemical communication may be used for such purposes as establishing dominance/submission relationships or else

indicating sexual availability and receptivity.

In many species a substance given off by one member serves to trigger off some specific behavior when smelled by another member of the same species. Such substances are termed *pheromones*, from the Greek words *pherein*, to transfer, and *hormon*, to excite. Perhaps the most striking use of pheromones occurs in the silk moth *Bombyx mori*. The female releases a substance from her abdomen

Below: A dog's organs of smell. Dogs have a much keener sense of smell than humans because the area occupied by their odor receptor sites is larger – about 200 million cells to humans' 10 million.

HOW A DOG SMELLS

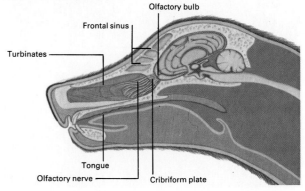

Olfactory bulb
Frontal sinus
Turbinates
Tongue
Olfactory nerve
Cribriform plate

that can be detected up to 1½ miles (2 km) down-wind by her male counterpart: only a few molecules of the pheromone need to impinge on the male's antennae for him to immediately start flying toward the female.

The human nose

The human organ of smell consists of two patches of sensory tissue which lie in small pits toward the back and top of two chambers – the *nasal cavities* – in the upper part of the nose. Air flowing up the nostrils and into these cavities is moistened by mucus secreted by the lining of the cavities and some of it is deflected upward over the olfactory area by the *turbinates* – bony plates in the walls of the chambers. Each patch covers an area of about 0.8 sq in. (500 sq mm) and is yellower than the membrane which surrounds it, and small and localized.

Each patch of olfactory tissue contains a large number of receptor cells, packed in a matrix of supporting cells. At their lower ends, the bodies of the receptor cells project downward from the matrix and bear six to eight fine hairs or cilia, surrounded by liquid mucus which covers the whole of the sensory area. For a substance to be smelled, it must give off molecules that can dissolve in this mucus when breathed into the nasal chambers; the molecules are then believed to excite the surfaces of the fine receptor cell hairs, triggering off *action*

potentials – electric signals in the receptor cells.

Once an action potential has been invoked, it travels upward along the surface of the receptor cell body, and from there along an axon which projects from the upper end of the cell body. Groups of axons from different receptors form a nerve cable which passes through a bony plate, called the *cribriform plate*, in the roof of the nasal cavity, and then enters one of the olfactory bulbs projecting from the brain. Electric messages transmitted along the axons can jump across the gaps, called *synapses*, between the ends of the axons and nerve cells within the olfactory bulbs, and from there are carried to smell centers in the brain.

The most widely accepted theory of how we distinguish different smells was postulated by the American scientist Amoore in the 1950s. He classified many smells into one of seven basic groups – musky, camphorous, minty, floral, ethereal, pungent and putrid – and showed that most of the substances producing any one of these smells had a common distinguishing feature. With the first five groups, the distinguishing feature was the substance's molecular shape, and with putrid and pungent smelling substances, its electric charge. He proposed that corresponding to the first five groups were five types of receptor site, each with a complementary shape to its respective odor molecule, such that each receptor would only accept substances within one group.

Left: The Pacific lobster has highly sensitive receptors in the hairs on its antennules and legs. Mounted on jointed stalks are its compound eyes, consisting of hundreds of lenses which enable the lobster to search for food and watch for enemies. The lobster crushes its prey with the larger claw and tears the food apart with the other.

According to Amoore's theory composite smells are produced by mixtures of substances that can stimulate two or more receptor types. Thus, the difference between the smell of Camembert and Danish Blue could be due to the relative proportion of pungent, putrid, musky and ethereal smelling substances given off by the two cheeses.

Although unproven, Amoore's theory is widely accepted in its general principles, and the idea that odor molecules actually lock into their corresponding receptor sites provides an explanation of the phenomenon of *adaptation* – the fact that even strong smells lose their impact after a few minutes – as once a particular set of receptors have been occupied, there is no longer room for further molecules to trigger off action potentials.

The odors of certain substances are influenced by factors other than the substance's effect on the receptor cells of the olfactory organ. For example, the irritating feeling caused by ammonia, the cool sensation caused by peppermint, and the tickling sensation of onions – all important features of their smells – are thought to be due to stimulation of pain, cold and heat receptors in the supporting cells of the olfactory organ.

The sense of smell strongly influences the sense of taste: vapors from food taken into the mouth waft upward to the olfactory organ and their detection adds subtle elaborations to the more basic taste sensations. This influence of smell on taste is appreciated most clearly when one has a heavy cold and the nasal cavities have become blocked.

Many of the interesting features of our sense of smell can be appreciated by examining which substances smell strongly and which ones are virtually odorless. Since olfaction operates through the inhalation of air containing odor molecules, one obvious property of smelly substances is that they must be either gases, volatile liquids, or capable of existing as fine suspensions in the air, perhaps dissolved in some other substance. A second important quality is that they must be water-soluble, since to gain access to the receptor hairs in the olfactory organ, they must first dissolve in the watery mucus that covers the hairs. A third quality is that they must have some rarity value; substances commonly impinging on the receptor cells of the olfactory organ cannot be smelled because any receptors for these substances would be permanently occupied. Fourthly, many smelly substances, though by no means all, carry some biologically significant message, for example they lead to sources of food or they warn of danger.

Putting these facts together, it can be seen why some substances have strong odors and others do not smell at all. Gases which form a significant proportion of the air we breathe, such as oxygen, nitrogen, carbon dioxide and the inert gases, are odorless, whereas less common and toxic gases, such

THE SENSE OF TASTE

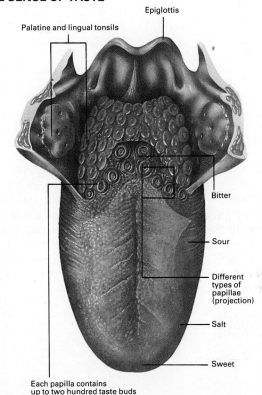

Palatine and lingual tonsils

Epiglottis

Bitter

Sour

Different types of papillae (projection)

Salt

Sweet

Each papilla contains up to two hundred taste buds

Above: The papillae on the tongue increase the area in contact with food and, except for those in the center, they contain numerous taste buds which, in turn, contain taste receptors distributed so that different parts of the tongue are sensitive to particular tastes.

as hydrogen sulfide, sulfur dioxide and ammonia, smell strongly. Inorganic solids with lattice structures, such as most salts and metals, as well as organic polymers and plastics consisting of long chains of molecules, cannot be smelled since their constituent atoms and molecules are strongly bound into the material.

Evolution

One striking feature of most smells is that they are usually either universally and instinctively liked or disliked: flower scents and cooking smells generally fall into the former category, the stink of rotting eggs into the latter. These positive and negative responses can be partly explained in terms of evolutionary pressures to avoid poisonous substances and to seek food sources: for example, individuals put off by the smell of rotting meat have survived better than individuals indifferent to the odor and have passed the trait on to their offspring.

See also: Cell; Eye; Pheromones; Skin; Smell.

Servomechanism

The word sevomechanism is derived from two roots: the Latin *servus* – a slave, and the Greek *mechanema* – a contrivance. Put together they suggest the concept of a slave mechanism, something which will perform a particular function with little effort from the controller.

Servomechanisms are defined as *closed-loop control systems* in which a small input power controls a much larger output power in a strictly proportional manner. The means by which this control is obtained may be mechanical, electric, hydraulic, pneumatic or electronic in any combination. In principle, control is effected by comparing the desired value to the actual value and the difference (or error) between them is then used to bring the actual value closer to the desired value. Many different servomechanisms may be brought together to form a complex AUTOMATIC CONTROL system to control, for example, a nuclear reactor or a chemical processing plant.

Today, servomechanism theory is well advanced and some theorists are considering its use outside engineering in the field of social science and economics, but here we are concerned only with its application to physical systems.

History

The history of servomechanisms is largely one of development and invention to solve some specific engineering problems. Thus engineers with a need to automatically control the speed of steam engines developed speed regulators, while the chemist developed temperature control for ovens and processes. The first servomechanism is credited to the Scot James Watt, who invented a GOVERNOR in 1775 to provide automatic speed regulation for a steam engine. In this two heavy balls are attached to the drive shaft of the engine in such a manner that they rotate with the shaft, moving away from the shaft as the speed increases, causing a sliding collar to move along the shaft.

This sliding-collar movement is connected via a

POSITION-CONTROL MECHANISM

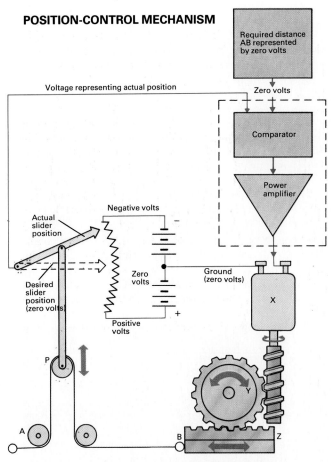

Required distance AB represented by zero volts

Zero volts

Comparator

Power amplifier

Voltage representing actual position

Negative volts

Actual slider position

Desired slider position (zero volts)

Zero volts

Positive volts

Ground (zero volts)

X

P

A

B

Y

Z

Left: Full Authority Control (FADEC) servomechanism units being fitted to a Lynx helicopter engine.
Above: A scheme for a position-control mechanism. A to B is the distance to be maintained. Any variation in the distance alters the slider, which sends a compensating voltage to X.

back was a specific example of the action of a servo-mechanism opened the way to the fundamentals of automatic control theory. The deep and far-reaching ideas developed to explain the behavior of electronic circuits could now be applied across the entire spectrum of servomechanisms.

All servomechanisms are control systems, but not all control systems are servomechanisms. Servomechanisms have two dominant features. First, the control is actuated by a quantity that is affected by the result of the control operation. Second, they allow a low-power unit to control a high-power operation at a distance. In regulators or self-operated controllers there is no separate control power, the force for the control action being derived from the controlled system.

Basic elements

Although the details vary according to the application, all servomechanisms consist of the same basic functional elements and work in the same manner. The set input is compared with the sensed output and the difference between these signals gives an error signal which is normally amplified and used to drive an actuator system. This actuator works to alter the controlled quantity, the value of which is measured by a feedback sensor to give the output signal supplied for comparison with the desired input. When the required setting has been achieved the input and output are equal, so there is no error signal to drive the actuator and movement stops. This sequence forms a closed loop; each of the operations affects and is dependent on the other.

The accuracy of such a control system depends on the precision with which the set input and achieved output can be measured and compared, and since these units do not have to handle the full power of the system they can be more readily produced to high standards of accuracy. Problems can occur if the output of the actuator system is not powerful enough to alter the output as required; this can be overcome by higher amplification of the error signal to give a greater operating force for a given error, so long as the actuator has sufficient capacity.

If the level of amplification is too great the actuator may overcorrect and drive the output beyond the required level. The control system will then act to reduce the set level, when the same effect may again occur to give an output value that is now less then required, leading to a further control action to increase the level, and so on. Such a sequence of over- and under-correction is known as *hunting*, and the system is unstable. This is clearly undesirable and various techniques are used to provide stability to the system. The simple system described above is proportional, the error signal being simply amplified to give the correcting action and one solution is to add damping to the system so as to slow

rod to the input steam valve. As the speed increases, so the extra movement of the collar decreases the amount of steam entering the engine, slowing it down; this causes the ball to move closer to the shaft and displaces the collar in the other direction, thus admitting more steam which causes the engine to speed up. The speed excursions and sliding collar movements diminish until the engine is running at a constant speed.

This and similar achievements in many different fields were to be the pattern of development of servo-mechanisms right up to the 1930s. That there is something fundamentally similar in all automatic control systems is a relatively new idea.

Perhaps the greatest contribution at this time to a fundamental theory of servomechanisms came from electronics. The theory of electronic amplifiers and associated circuits was developing very quickly. The principle of negative FEEDBACK was established, and the realization that negative feed-

POWER-ASSISTED RUDDER CONTROL

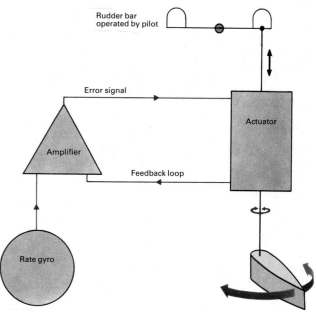

Left: Assembling a sophisticated electronic control unit for an aircraft gas turbine.
Above: In a basic power-assisted rudder control mechanism, a rate gyro determines the rate of turn of the aircraft, and effectively maintains the course required by the pilot.

and smooth the output fluctuations. Alternatively, a control unit may be used to modify the error signal so as to obtain the required actuator response.

Servomechanisms may be entirely mechanical in character, but electric sensors and actuators are more often used. Hydraulic and pneumatic systems are also employed for some applications.

Applications

The applications of servomechanisms are to be found in many industries. For example, the modern airplane could not fly without using these devices. Consider the strain on a pilot who has to fly a set course on a particular compass bearing and has to contend with a variable cross wind. The physical strain of flying with a few degrees of rudder would be intolerable after a short time. One way of solving this problem is to use actuators.

The pilot flies onto course and switches on the servomechanism consisting of the rate gyro, amplifier, actuator and feedback loop. From now on the gyro senses any deviation of the airplane from the original course and adjusts the length of the actuator. This has the effect of shortening or lengthening the control rod to the rudder, and so moving it one way or the other to remedy the deviation. The stabilizer is designed to have only a limited effect, say five degrees, of rudder deflection

and is capable of being overridden by the pilot at any time. Actuators can be fitted to all the control surfaces of an airplane, but they are not the same as automatic pilots.

An autopilot is a more complex mechanism which will sense yaw, pitch and roll and will fly an airplane to a particular height at a particular speed on a particular heading.

The first servo system is controlled by the rate gyro plus another unit, which is connected also to the rudder bar and consists of a heading gyro and another actuator, amplifier and feedback loop. The second actuator is capable of much greater movement and can exercise complete yaw control of the airplane in response to the signals from the heading gyro. When the autopilot is switched on, the pilot has no need to control the airplane, as similar control can be exercised over the other flying control surfaces deriving their signals from the artificial horizon, the altimeter and similar instruments.

Only a few examples of servomechanisms have been described. They should, however, have given an idea of the variety of duties for which these devices may be used, and which could hardly be accomplished otherwise.

See also: Feedback; Governor; Gyroscope; Hydraulic mechanism; Linear electric motor.

Sewage treatment

In countries where water is plentiful and cheap, people often tend to abuse it, using much more than they really need. It is used for drinking, bathing, washing clothes and automobiles, for many different purposes in industry, and finally, after it has been used, it is thrown away down a toilet, a waste pipe or some convenient drain. In industrialized countries, each person on average uses between 50 and 100 gallons (227–455 l) of water per day, and rivers and streams would be in a terrible state if all that water were allowed to reach them in a dirty condition, bringing with it a load of filth and waste materials.

The need for something to be done about the cleaning up of the population's waste waters, or sewage as it is generally called, became apparent around the time of the Industrial Revolution. Initially the ability of organisms, normally present in soil, to remove or stabilize polluting matter was used extensively. For example, organic matter of animal origin contains nitrogen, often tied up in a complex form, but the soil organisms are able to break down the complexes and incorporate the nitrogen into the soil itself. So, by irrigating sewage onto land a certain amount of purification of the water was effected. But any good gardener knows that continuous fertilizing of land will upset the balance in the soil unless suitable crops are grown as part of the cycle – and so the term sewage farm became part of the language. Roughly, at least 100 acres (40.1 hectares) of land would be required for each one million gallons (4.5 million l) per day of sewage to be dealt with (which would be the sewage from a population of about 20,000).

When limited amounts of sewage are discharged into running water the natural biological processes oxidize the organic matter and act to reduce bacterial

Below: This sewage treatment plant at Al Ain, Abu Dhabi, includes a final stage to make the effluent suitable for reuse for irrigation purposes.

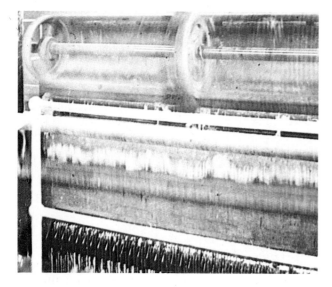

contamination to give a reasonably clean water flow a relatively short distance downstream of the discharge. With larger sewage flows the oxygen dissolved in the water is insufficient to clear the organic matter and pollution rapidly builds up. A measure of the strength of sewage is given by its Biochemical Oxygen Demand (BOD) which is determined by a standard laboratory procedure, and a major aim of sewage treatment is to reduce the BOD of the final discharge to an acceptable level (normally set by regulatory authorities).

Sewage itself consists of dirty water containing not only impurities in solution, but also in the colloidal state, in the form of fine sediment and as bulky solid matter, originating as it does from washbasins, toilets, bathrooms, kitchens, and a whole range of industrial processes. The water simply acts as a vehicle for the polluting matter and is not itself changed, so that in theory it ought to be possible to remove the polluting matter and restore the water to its original pure condition; in practice about 90 per cent purification is achieved.

Treatment works

In a typical modern treatment works, the raw sewage is first passed through *bar screens* to remove bulky solids which are either incinerated or are macerated (softened) and put back into the sewage flow. The next step is to remove grit, which might otherwise damage pumps and other equipment, by passing the sewage through *constant velocity channels* which are of parabolic cross section to give a constant flow rate of 1 ft/s. At this speed the grit settles out and can be removed for land disposal while organic matter is carried on in the flow.

The sewage is next passed through primary sedimentation tanks where the finer sediment separates out and settles to the bottom as sludge, from where it is removed possibly twice daily, and thickened up a little in consolidation tanks before being pumped to a mechanical dewatering plant. Here it is conditioned with chemicals and pressed to form a partly dried cake which is finally disposed of as a fertilizer on farm land. Alternatively the consolidated sludge may undergo heated, *anaerobic* (in the absence of free oxygen) digestion in large digesters, where the organisms break down the fatty matter and some organic material, thus changing the sludge and rendering it inoffensive and ready to be sprayed on land as a fertilizer. A byproduct of digestion is a gas rich in methane, which is collected and used for heating and power production purposes. Where sludge disposal is a problem it may be dried and then incinerated.

The settled sewage passing over the weirs of the sedimentation tanks is subjected to biological oxidation either in biological filters or by the Activated Sludge Process described below. In either

Top: A fine bar screen removes bulky solids from the incoming sewage. The rotating brush at the top keeps the screen-clearing rake clean.
Above: The grit-collecting trough of a constant-velocity channel; organic matter flows straight on.

• FACT FILE •

- 1858 was known as the year of the great stink in London, because of the foul condition of the sewage-polluted River Thames. Cholera deaths at this time exceeded 20,000 per annum, and were chiefly attributable to a lack of an adequate waste-disposal system.

- Britain has one of the densest sewer systems in the world, with more than 248,560 miles (400,000 km) of sewer pipes; much of it is now due for replacement.

- The Chicago Tunnels and Reservoirs plan is designed to deal with a pollution problem that has turned the Chicago River and Lake Michigan into virtual cesspits. Chicago produces more than 1500 million gallons of sewage per day in dry weather, and effluent can reach 60,000 million gallons per day during severe storms.

- Remotely controlled sewer-pipe crawlers are used to monitor the internal condition of many sewer pipes. The crawlers are in fact cylindrical cameras mounted on runners, and relay pictures of pipe internal surfaces back to a control unit such as a specially equipped van for detailed examination.

volume (clinker, hard coke and blast-furnace slag are all first class). Settled sewage, when sprayed evenly onto the surface of this medium, leads to the establishment on the filter medium of a slime film that contains colonies of the necessary biological organisms to oxidize the impurities in the sewage to stable substances. For example, carbonaceous matter is oxidized to carbon dioxide, and nitrogen first to nitrite and finally nitrate. The idea is to create an environment in which the organisms can live, do their job and propagate, and once established, a filter bed will continue to function literally for ever unless it suffers physical breakdown or damage from external causes.

In addition to the bacterial organisms in the slime, percolating filters tend to have algae and other plant growths which can be carried out of the

Below: Part of a primary sedimentation tank; the floor-cleaning blade has been lowered to remove any remaining sedimentation from the tank.
Bottom: Rotating scraper blades cleaning the floor of a circular, final sedimentation tank.

case, the impurities in solution are oxidized and stabilized and the effluent then passes through final settling tanks to remove any sediment which may have been formed. This sediment, which contains the organisms that break down the sewage, is returned to the system to keep the biological processes going. At this stage, the effluent is often fit to discharge to the river, but where very high standards are to be complied with, this effluent would be further treated to remove the last traces of suspended matter by passing through sand filters or through microstrainers, where the aperture in the mesh can be as small as 0.0009 in. (23 micrometers). The effluent is now probably cleaner than the river water into which it discharges.

Biological filters

The most common type of biological filter is the percolating filter which consists of a basin with side walls between 5 and 6 ft (1.5 to 1.8 m) deep and a slightly sloping floor to permit free drainage. The basin is filled with some durable material, preferably with pores to give a large surface area per unit

Left: A major junction in the sewer network under London, England. Specially constructed sewer systems were virtually unheard of until the nineteenth century, when they were built in large cities, such as Boston and New York in the U.S., and London and Paris in Europe. Before then, waste was usually simply thrown into streets or into the nearest river – a method of disposal which constituted a major health hazard.

filter. The flow is accordingly passed through sedimentation or humus tanks to collect this material before the water is discharged.

Activated sludge

In the Activated Sludge Process the settled sewage is mixed with activated sludge, which is a suspension of coagulated matter on which live the organisms necessary for the biological purification of the sewage. The mixture (*mixed liquor*) is passed through specially designed tanks where air is supplied, either by blowing compressed air through fine diffusers or by mechanical means, using rotors which cause air to be taken in from the atmosphere. The sewage and organisms are kept in intimate contact for about nine or ten hours, during which time the impurities are biologically oxidized and stabilized. The activated sludge is allowed to settle out in tanks and the clear effluent passes forward to be returned to the river.

Other systems

One of the simplest forms of sewage disposal, used mainly in remote rural areas for the disposal of residential and agricultural sewage, is the *cesspool*. This is a tank or pit, watertight to prevent leakage into watercourses, into which the sewage is drained. It is emptied two or three times per month, and the effluent is used as manure, often after chemical

deodorization and the addition of lime or bleaching powder to kill the unwanted organisms.

A more effective method for handling the sewage from domestic sources is the *septic tank*. The sewage takes about 16 to 24 hours to pass through the tank, where it is decomposed by anaerobic bacteria. The sludge settles at the bottom of the tank, which is emptied when it is a third to a half full of sludge, removing about two thirds of the sludge and leaving the rest to maintain the bacterial activity in the tank. It was originally thought that this process would destroy pathogenic (disease-producing) bacteria, but this is now known to be untrue.

In coastal areas, sewage is often discharged directly into the sea without any form of treatment, but increasing use is now being made of methods of diluting or disinfecting the sewage to reduce the pollution of coastal waters. One simple method is the use of *comminutors*, machines which trap the suspended solids in the sewage and cut them into small pieces to speed up dispersal and decomposition. The effluent is thoroughly diluted at the discharge point to prevent excessive local pollution.

A more advanced system is the *electrolytic process*, in which seawater is electrolyzed and mixed with the sewage before it is discharged into the sea.

See also: Electrolysis; Oxygen; Pollution control; Waste disposal; Water; Water supply.

Sewing machine

The sewing machine works on a different principle from that of hand sewing. In hand sewing, the needle and the free end of the thread are passed right through the fabric and pulled through to the other side. No normal sewing machine could do this, because its needle is attached to the mechanism and cannot be released. Furthermore, hand sewing is done with a limited length of thread, the whole of which is pulled through the fabric at each stitch (except for the part that has already formed stitches). This would not be practical for a high-speed machine, which must be able to draw thread continuously from a spool or bobbin.

There are now a few highly complex machines which can imitate hand sewing, thanks to a free-floating double-pointed needle and other devices, but the most popular designs of the machine use either chain stitch or lock stitch.

Chain stitch

In the simplest form of chain stitch, only one thread is used. This thread is pulled off a reel above the fabric and threaded through the eye of the needle; some machines have a built-in needle threader for automatic threading. All sewing machine needles have the eye at the same end as the point.

The needle enters the fabric, pulling a loop of thread through with it. It then withdraws slightly, but friction against the fabric prevents the thread from withdrawing, so that it broadens out into a loop under the fabric. A *looper* – basically an oscillating hook – then comes across and catches the loop, after which the needle withdraws fully and the fabric moves on one stitch length.

The looper holds the loop under the fabric in such a position that when the needle descends again, it passes through the held loop before forming a new loop, which is caught in turn by the looper. Thus a succession of loops is formed under the fabric, each one laced through the previous one.

Lock stitch

Two threads are used in basic lock stitch, one above the fabric, pulled continuously off a spool, and the other below it, taken from a small bobbin mounted in a bobbin case or *shuttle*. The upper thread, or needle thread, is carried down through the fabric as before, but the loop it forms is caught by a hook traveling on a curved path (either oscillating or revolving fully) which passes the loop around the bobbin, looping it around the bobbin thread.

The needle then withdraws, pulling the intersection of the threads into the fabric. In this way a stitch is created which looks the same from above and below; each thread runs across the surface of the fabric and dips into it at intervals to loop around the other thread halfway through the fabric.

Right: The Pfaff synchromatic 1216 sewing machine is one of the latest designs which bring to home sewing a sophistication that some industrial machines lack. This machine, for example, incorporates a foot control for speed regulation, mechanisms enabling button holes to be sewn in sequence and allowing stitch density to be regulated, and an overlock switch for the sewing and finishing of seams.

Relative merits

Chain stitch can be executed quickly, typically at 7000 stitches per minute, corresponding to 8 ft (2.4 m) per second at 12 stitches to the inch. Lock stitch cannot match this speed because it puts a greater strain on the thread. But single-thread chain stitch can be unraveled by simply pulling apart the end of an unfinished seam, or cutting one stitch and pulling. It is therefore only used on certain industrial machines where this does not matter, such as button sewers and tacking machines. It was also used on the earliest machines. Other chain stitch machines use two-thread chain stitch, where a separate underthread is interlooped with the ordinary loops under the fabric, making the stitch secure.

This, however, results in excessively high thread consumption: about five inches of thread are used for every inch of seam.

Lock stitch is secure and uses about half as much thread, but its use is restricted not only by its maximum speed, but also by the fact that the needle thread has to pass right around the bobbin at each stitch. This makes it impossible for the bobbin thread to be drawn from a large fixed spool and since the size of the bobbin is restricted by the size of the loop that can be drawn from the needle thread, its capacity is severely limited. (The underthread for two-thread chain stitch, however, can be drawn from a fixed spool.) For this reason, lock stitch is most suitable for home sewing machines, where

ROTARY LOCK-STITCH SEWING MACHINE

Fixed thread guide
Thread tensioning discs
Linkage to drive needle bar and thread take-up lever
Upper shaft
Thread take-up lever
Two cams to move feed dog
Toothed belt drives lower shaft at double speed
Belt driven by motor through transmission
Guides for needle bar
Needle bar
Fixed thread guides
Needle
Feed dog motion linkage
Upper thread
Presser foot
Feed dog
Gear drive for rotary hook
Bobbin and rotary hook (turns twice as fast as rest of machine)
Linkage to move feed dog from side to side
Linkage to move feed dog up and down

Above: The basic mechanical system of a rotary lock-stitch machine.

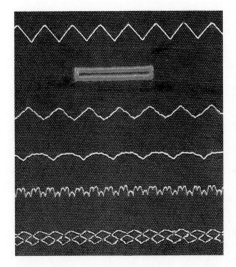

Above left: A great diversity of stitch patterns is available on some of today's sewing machines. Above right: The control panel of a Pfaff machine.

speed and thread capacity are less important than in industry, where chain stitch is generally preferred. Chain stitch was also used in many home machines during the nineteenth century.

Feed

The fabric is advanced at each stitch by a *feed* mechanism, which consists of a toothed bar under the fabric, gripping it by pressing it up against a smooth spring-loaded *presser foot*. The feed bar moves in a *four-stop motion*: up, forward, down, back and so on. This can normally be reversed to move the fabric the other way (securing the end of the seam by back stitching) and its travel can be altered to change the length of the stitch.

History

The first patent for a sewing machine was taken out in 1790 by Thomas Saint, a London, England, cabinet maker. It used single-thread chain stitch, and had a forked needle which went through a hole previously made by an awl. It was probably never built, since minor design faults in the patent specification would have made it unworkable.

In 1810, a German, B. Krems, invented the eye-pointed needle, again without commercial success, but the first commercial machine was built in France by Barthélémy Thimonnier, a tailor, and had a barbed needle which tended to catch in the cloth. It also had no feed and the fabric was moved by hand, but nevertheless, Thimonnier set up a business making military uniforms, and operated successfully until his machines were destroyed by hand workers who feared they would lose their jobs. After this setback, Thimonnier abandoned any further development of his design.

The first lock-stitch machine was invented in the early 1830s in New York by Walter Hunt. Again, it was not commercially exploited, but in 1846 Elias Howe patented a fairly similar machine. It had an inconvenient feed mechanism whereby the edge of the cloth was held vertically on spikes on a *baster plate*, which then carried it through the machine. At the end of its travel the baster plate had to be moved back and the next length of cloth put on the spikes. Moreover, the machine needed a specially curved needle.

The first machine to have the general form of a modern one was produced by the American Isaac M. Singer in 1851. It was a lock-stitch machine with a straight, vertically sliding needle and a spring-

Below: Jam-proof rotary hooks, found on many of today's sewing machines, insure perfect stitch formation, whatever the sewing speed.

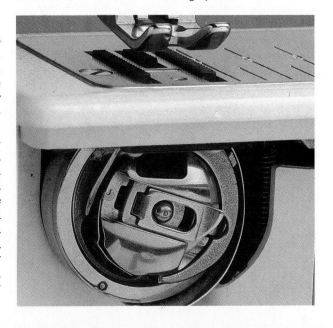

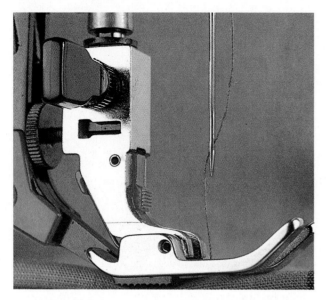

Above: The built-in dual feed mechanism on this Pfaff machine evenly feeds in the upper and lower layers of fabric with no shifting of the material. It copes with low-friction materials, such as silk.
Right: Thimonnier's 1830 chain-stitch machine. The fabric was fed through the machine by hand.

loaded presser foot. It was the first machine to be foot-powered by a treadle.

Another American, Allen B. Wilson, invented in 1852 the rotary hook, which took the needle thread around a stationary bobbin (Singer's machine had had a straight-line oscillating shuttle). In 1854 he invented the four-motion feed. This completed the basic equipment of the modern machine, and later improvements were mainly in detail.

Modern machines

Most modern household machines have a swing needle which produces a zigzag stitch. There is an elongated hole in the needle plate under the fabric, and the needle moves left and right at alternate stitches. The width of zigzag can be set from zero (straight stitch) to 0.2 or 0.3 in. (5 or 7 mm). Adjusting the stitch length can give a long, loose zigzag for sewing stretch fabrics or finishing raw edges to stop fraying, or a very short, tight one, for making buttonholes or doing *satin stitch*, which is a simple embroidery stitch. If the forward motion is completely stopped, the machine will sew on buttons or make *bar tacks* (reinforcements at points of strain). The zigzag can also be used for *blind hemming* (turning up the bottom of a garment so that stitches do not show from the outside) by folding the fabric, right sides (outsides) together, and stitching so that the point of each zigzag just catches the fold without passing through the thickness of the fabric.

Fancy stitches are produced by CAM boxes which vary the width of the zigzag and the direction of the feed in a set pattern.

Industrial machines perform all these functions and more, but are larger and heavier, and tend to be specialized one-function machines, such as buttonholers. They also nearly all use chain stitch. There are many complex multiple versions of chain stitch for extra strong stitching on heavy fabrics; up to nine threads may be used at once.

Automatic control has begun to enter the clothing industry, and many machines are programed to do complete operations by themselves, for example making shirt collars. There have been experiments with threadless machines with hollow needles which inject a fluid into the material to be sewn – this is hardened by heat treatment to form a seam. But these are really no longer sewing machines.

See also: Carpet manufacture; Clothing manufacture; Hosiery manufacture.

Sextant

Since the earliest ocean voyages navigators have had to fix their position at sea by means of measuring the angles above the horizon of heavenly bodies, the Sun, Moon and stars. The simplest, and least accurate, of these is to measure the altitude (angle above the horizon) of the Pole Star (in the Northern Hemisphere). More accurately, the altitude of the Sun at local noon, or of bright stars whose position is known at their highest point, will give the latitude after simple calculations from tables.

The first instruments to be used for measuring these angles were astrolabes, cross staffs, back staffs and quadrants – all variations on the theme of a sighting bar moved along a scale of degrees. In most cases it was necessary to view both the star and the horizon at the same time from the deck of the ship, and it is not surprising that the observations were inaccurate. In the case of the quadrant the reference point was not the horizon but a plumb line attached to the scale. This made it possible to concentrate on the star only, but the plumb line could easily swing about, leading to further errors.

The device which replaced these instruments, the forerunner of the sextant, was the reflecting octant invented by the Englishman, John Hadley, in 1731. The principle and design of the octant was the same as that of any sextant in daily use today: the main difference is that the octant had a scale which was one-eighth of a circle, 45 degrees, and a sextant has a scale of one-sixth of a circle, 60 degrees. Because both devices measure an angle which is reflected by a mirror, the octant will measure angles up to 90 degrees and the sextant angles up to 120 degrees.

Hadley's invention was to use a pair of small mirrors to reflect the image of the star to be observed so that it appeared to be on the horizon. The navigator could keep both in view at the same time, and as the ship rolled both would move together. The movable mirror was attached to the pivot of the movable index bar, at the radius of the scale or *arc*, so that as the angle was changed the mirror would move. This mirror reflected the star's image to a second mirror, permanently set to view the first one. The navigator looked through a sight to the second mirror, past which he could see the horizon. He moved the first by moving the index bar until the star's image reflected by both mirrors exactly touched the horizon. The angle was then read off the arc, which was graduated in degrees (but twice as closely as a true scale of degrees, to allow for the mirror's reflection).

Hadley's octant was immediately accepted by navigators. In 1757, John Campbell introduced the true sextant, which was capable of measuring a greater angle. Captain Cook, the English explorer, was probably the first to fully apply the potential of the sextant for measuring not only vertical angles but also angles at any inclination. By measuring the angle between the Moon and a given star, he could calculate the precise time, using tables of the Moon's motion, enabling him to find his longitude as well as latitude – the method used for the charting of New Zealand during the voyage of 1768–71. The invention of accurate timekeepers made the procedure unnecessary, and the sextant was then

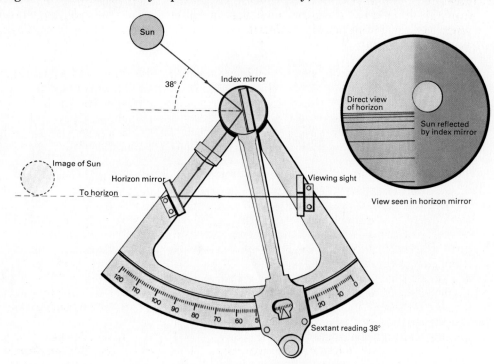

Right: The basic layout of a sextant, an instrument for measuring the angle of stars or the Sun at precise times to give position at sea. The procedure is to move the index mirror until the bottom of the image of the Sun or star just touches the line of the horizon, as shown in the inset. This reading is corrected to give the position of the center of the Sun or star.

Left: An early model of a sextant. This nautical instrument was introduced in the eighteenth century and revolutionized travel by enabling accurate mapping of the world. Above: The general design of the sextant has not changed, although advanced optical technology has made it possible to shorten the telescope.

used to measure the altitude of stars or the Sun at precise times, thus giving the longitude whenever it was required.

Although the earliest sextants and octants had simple sighting devices, the accuracy was much improved by the use of a small telescope instead. The second mirror, the horizon mirror, would only be silvered across half its width so that the telescope would show both the horizon and the star side by side. Dark filters could be moved into the light paths to cut down the brightness of the Sun or horizon.

The sextant has remained basically unchanged from 1800 to the present day, but there have been some changes to the way in which the arm of the sextant is made to travel along the arc. In the early days there was no fine-adjustment screw and the navigator merely moved the arm along the arc and clamped it to the frame so that the reading could be taken. On a moving deck this was rather hard to do, so in the 1760s a fine-adjustment tangent screw was added. This meant that the operator could quickly take his sight to the nearest degree and then, by using the tangent screw, make the final close adjustment. The only drawback with the clamping type of sextant was that the tangent screw frequently had to be returned to its starting position, otherwise it would come to the limit of its thread as a sighting was being taken. The problem was solved in the 1920s. A toothed rack was cut into the sextant frame and the tangent screw was now meshed into this. The arm could be moved along the arc by pressing a quick-release catch, and the tangent screw could travel the full length of the arc without needing to be reset.

The sextants of this period were still using the finely engraved scale, which had to be read with a magnifier, as they had been over the previous 100 years. Around 1933 the *micrometer* sextant was evolved which is still in use today. Instead of engraving the fine divisions on the arc, they were transferred to an enlarged tangent screw head, doing away with the magnifier and making the sextant easier to read.

Other types

The sextant may still be used for air navigation far from the busy air corridors. In this case the horizon cannot be used as it is below the true horizontal, and a system which reflects the image of a bubble level into the field of view is used. *Astrodomes*, small transparent domes into which the sextant will fit, may be set into the top of the airplane, or in the case of the faster airplane a periscope system will be fitted. Land sextants, in which the horizon is provided by a small trough of mercury in the sextant, have been made.

See also: Inertial guidance; Navigation.